LOVE IS A FRENZY

GW00320392

As a nightclub singer, Rachel was used to men's admiration—but seventeen-year-old Nicky Hammond was something different. His boyish admiration was sweet and touching—but Rachel couldn't possibly take it seriously, let alone return it; yet how could she make Nicky see that without hurting him? And how could she convince his disapproving father Mark that she wasn't cradle-snatching—or worse?

LOVE IS A FRENZY

BY

CHARLOTTE LAMB

MILLS & BOON LIMITED
17–19 FOLEY STREET
LONDON W1A 1DR

First published 1979
Australian copyright 1979
Philippine copyright 1979
This edition 1979

© Charlotte Lamb 1979

ISBN 0 263 73123 5

Set in Linotype Baskerville 10 on 12 pt.

Made and printed in Great Britain by
Richard Clay (The Chaucer Press), Ltd., Bungay, Suffolk

CHAPTER ONE

SHE recognised him at once. 'An absolute bastard', Nicky had called him, and the description fitted like a glove. Without having spoken to him she knew exactly what she could expect from him, his blue eyes roaming over her in insolent appraisal, the hard mouth cynically sensual. The blue-white spotlight spun around her, the club air filled with drifting tendrils of smoke. She crossed her long, golden-brown legs and a few whistles went up. As she leaned back on the piano her wry gaze met Derry's and he winked at her, silently mouthing, 'Get 'em, baby!' He played the opening bars and with her eyes fixed on him she let her lashes flicker meaningfully towards the man leaning back in his chair at the last table on the right. Derry and she had long had a series of silent signals set up and he shot a shrewd glance in that direction. His face registered nothing. He looked back at her and there was irritation in his hazel eyes.

Her song was one Derry had written for her, a compound of sultry sexiness and humour, the words witty and clever, the music purringly sweet. Derry was talented, there was no doubt about that, but all his gifts were marred by his refusal to be serious. He was a magician, producing bright, impressive work which was yet somehow plastic, artificial. 'He's a phoney,' Martin had said, with sadness rather than disgust, because for all Derry's insincerity there was charm and amiability in him. People always liked him. His smile was reflected in his eyes. He could be kind. He was often thoughtful. In a way, Rachel thought, it was Derry's misfortune to be so flawed rather than anything culpable in him.

At the table nearest the stage sat Nicky, his dreaming head propped on his hands, his eyes adoringly on her. As she finished singing and the applause broke out, she let a smile touch her mouth and looked at him. His blue eyes glowed. She let Derry lift her down from her seat on the piano. Hand in hand they bowed and went off stage as the lights lowered. A comedian went on, patting Rachel's shapely rear with a whispered, 'Great kid!' She murmured back, 'Good luck, Rob,' then followed Derry down the narrow corridor to the dressing-room.

The door shut and Derry turned on her. 'You've left it too late! I warned you. I bet they have that kid shadowed everywhere he goes. With all that money at stake you can be sure they don't let him take a step that Daddy doesn't know about.'

'Be quiet, Derry,' she said calmly, sitting down in front of the mirror and beginning to remove her stage make-up.

Derry watched her skilful movements irritably. 'Darling, he's worth millions! And he's nuts about you. He sits out there night after night eating you with those soulful eyes of his, and you have to be dumb to let a fish that size get away from you.'

She peeled off her false eyelashes. 'Derry, the boy isn't even eighteen yet. Talk sense, for God's sake. He's a very sweet boy, but I can give him seven years.' Her green eyes filled with laughter. 'Poor Nicky! He has a crush on me and I'm flattered. One day he'll be a very good-looking young man, but right now he's a seventeen-year-old walking around in a dream.'

'And you're the dream,' Derry told her. He wore the frustrated, impatient look he had worn often lately; ever since Nicky Hammond walked into the club, in fact, and Derry first saw the possibility the boy represented. Derry's whole life had been spent looking for the impossible dream. He was a gambler, most of his money going on horses, roulette, cards, but he had that streak of greed in him, a desire to get something for nothing. He was staring at Rachel now as if he could take her neck in his hands and wring it. 'You like him, I can see you do whenever you smile at him. He would marry you tomorrow if you gave him the green light.'

'Of course I like him,' Rachel sighed, becoming faintly weary. 'I've told you—he's a sweet boy. I'm touched by the way he looks at me. But I have no intention of marrying him.' She stood up. 'I want to dress, Derry. Out!'

His weak, handsome mouth compressed and he groaned. 'You little mule! I wish I could beat some sense into your head.' Then he went out and she stepped out of her glittering stage costume, standing in bra and briefs as she hung it very carefully among the others behind the curtain. A click brought her head round, the light glinting on gold strands in her chestnut hair.

A man's broad shoulders filled the doorway. Dazed, her eyes slid up the lean, formidable length of him to the watchful face. He wore evening dress, immaculate, expensively cut, a fresh white carnation in his lapel. His features had the cutting edge of a razor, the brown flesh tight over angular bones, and despite the sensuality of that mouth there was no hint of any weakness anywhere.

'Would you mind leaving while I dress?' she asked in a cold, polite voice.

· He smiled and a chill ran down her spine. Coming into the room, he closed the door.

Aware of the fact that those insulting blue eyes were taking in every detail of her half-naked body, she furiously dragged down a wrap and thrust her arms into it, tying it tightly around her waist with a jerk.

'I told you to leave!'

He smiled again, mockery in his face. 'My son has better taste than I'd suspected.' The deep, drawling voice was infuriatingly pleasant on the ear, but what he was saying was in no way pleasant.

'I'm dressing. No one is allowed backstage.'

He leaned against the door and slid a hand into his jacket. Fuming, Rachel watched him begin to light a cigar, the aromatic smoke curling around his face. 'Go ahead,' he drawled. 'I'm sure you're very accustomed to taking your clothes off in male company.'

Heat burned in her cheeks. Then green eyes flashed. 'Mr Hammond, I don't know what your son has told you ...'

He laughed. 'My son has told me nothing.' There was no humour in that laughter. Sardonic malice sparkled in his eyes. 'I'm sure you warned him to keep his mouth shut about you.'

'I did nothing of the kind!'

'No?' Mark Hammond gave her a derisive look.

'No!'

'Come, Miss Austen, you're smarter than that! You

knew that once I found out what Nicky was up to I would lock him up and throw away the key.'

'You talk as though he was a child!' Rachel burst out, trembling with anger.

'A precocious one,' Mark Hammond drawled, and again the blue eyes flicked over her from her bright rich hair to her long legs. 'And apparently one with a taste for luxury items.' He looked into her angry eyes. 'Did it amuse you to initiate my son? He's a pretty boy. A little sheltered for his age, perhaps.' He shrugged. 'I'm sure you've had fun teaching him some of the facts of life.'

Rachel had never been so angry in her life. She looked at this black-haired stranger with bitter distaste and rage. 'You're under a misapprehension, Mr Hammond,' she flared. 'Nicky doesn't see me like that! He ...'

'Don't tell me you haven't come across yet?' he asked mockingly. 'Were you waiting for the price to go up? Isn't that too bad? So the diamond bracelet wasn't big enough bait? Poor Nicky! Disappointing for him.' He turned and opened the door. Over his broad shoulder he smiled coldly at her. 'Goodbye, Miss Austen.'

She threw a jar of cold cream at the door. It smashed and the sticky white ooze spread across the panels and down to the floor, the glass embedded in it. Tears spurted from her eyes, tears of temper and chagrin.

She sat down and stared at her own reflection, seeing the gleam of her hair, the oval creamy face, the well-shaped, generous mouth. For one second she almost wished she had encouraged Nicky Hammond, then she grimaced at herself. She had never felt anything but pity, kindness and affection for the boy. For all the enormous fortune he would one day inherit, he seemed to her a case for compassion—the only son of a multi-millionaire, yet in many ways one of the most deprived children she had ever met.

He had walked into the club a month ago with a party of noisy, wild young people of his own class and kind. They had been celebrating some birthday. The girl whose birthday it was had kittenish yellow curls and a silly, excitable little face. She drank far too much during the evening, and when Rachel came on to sing she had gone on giggling and calling out throughout the song. It was not an unusual situation. Rachel went on singing calmly, although she found it irritating to have to compete with that sort of silliness.

She had not noticed Nicky Hammond at the time, but afterwards he had come round to the dressing-room to apologise. Derry had been in the room, drinking an ice-cold beer, and she had been surprised by his smiling friendliness. The gangling boy in an obviously well-tailored suit had been just the kind of visitor to bring out Derry's sarcasm normally. Instead, he had smoothed over the earlier incident, grinned easily at their visitor and drifted off, leaving her alone with the boy.

Nicky's dark hair was over-long, rather curly, his blue eyes fever-bright as he watched her. The angularity of his face and the long bones made it clear that he would one day be a very tall, lean man, but now he was a clumsy boy whose movements were not yet co-ordinated into any sort of grace, plunging like a wild horse without being able to control his own limbs. His flushed skin and husky voice had told her clearly enough that he found her attractive. She had been touched by his obvious admiration. There was an innocent sincerity in his gaze which was flattering, although she was used to male admiration.

He had asked her tentatively about Derry. 'Your pianist ... is he your husband?'

Rachel had smiled. 'My cousin,' she had told him frankly. 'We grew up together. I was orphaned when I was eight and Derry's parents took me in to their home. Derry is more of a brother than a cousin, I suppose.'

Nicky had beamed. 'You're fond of him?'

'Very.' She had ran a hand into her loose chestnut hair. 'What about you, Nicky? Have you any brothers and sisters?'

There had been an odd look in his face for a moment. She had almost imagined that it was a look of calculation, but in such a young boy it couldn't have been. 'No,' he had told her. 'I'm an only child.'

'Do your parents live in London?'

The flush on his face had grown deeper. 'My father is in the States just now,' he had said. 'My mother is dead.'

From the start she had found it easy to talk to him. Casually, she had asked, 'Your father is a businessman?'

He had nodded and asked quickly, 'How long have you been singing?'

'Since I was sixteen,' she had told him, and then at the unasked question in his transparent eyes she had added gently, 'I'm twenty-five now. How old are you, Nicky?'

His tongue had jammed in his mouth as he tried

to lie to her and it was then that she began to feel this curious warm compassion for him. 'Twenty,' he had finally mumbled.

Rachel could have kissed him. Gently she had said, 'Now tell me the truth. Or shall I guess? Eighteen?'

For a second or two he had looked furious, then he had given her a shy, appealing grin. 'Well, nearly,' he had said.

'You look older,' she had lied, eyes warm, seeing how easy it would be to hurt this curiously vulnerable boy.

He had stood up, shuffling his feet. 'Will you have dinner with me?' he had plunged hoarsely, eyes on his shoes.

Hesitating, she had wondered how to phrase a refusal, then a look at his tense features had softened her into replying, 'Why don't you have lunch with Derry and myself? I'm a good cook. I'll make you my own speciality—hotpot.' The green eyes had been teasing. 'Cheap and nourishing and it doesn't need constant supervision.'

'Oh,' he had said, eyes shining. 'Thank you.' He darted off and came back with a stumbling rush. 'When? Where do you live?'

'Tomorrow,' she had found herself saying. 'Derry and I share a flat in Kensington.' She had written down the address, adding, 'Twelve o'clock. Don't be earlier, because we get up late.'

Telling Derry later that night, she had wondered if he would blow his top, but he seemed oddly amused and satisfied. 'Hotpot?' he had echoed. 'Rubbish! Give the kid a fancy meal. A great cook shouldn't hide her light under hotpot.'

Rachel had frowned, looking at him sharply.

'You don't know who he is?' Derry had asked, still grinning.

'Nicky something or other,' she had told him. 'I didn't catch the surname.'

'Hammond,' Derry had murmured very softly, watching her face.

It had meant nothing to her.

Observing the blankness of her features, Derry had filled in the bare outline. 'Son of Mark Hammond, the oil man, and heir to billions. For heaven's sake, Ray, even you must have heard of the Hammond Corporation?'

She had sat down very suddenly, going pale. 'Nicky is that Hammond's son?' She had never connected the name because it seemed so incredible that someone of that class should be coming into the Harem, a London night club without pretensions of exclusivity. A vague memory teased her. 'But doesn't Mark Hammond own the Harem?'

'He owns the whole damned hotel block,' Derry had said cheerfully. 'But he's so rich I doubt if he even remembers.'

She put her hands to her face. 'And I've invited his son to take hotpot with us? Oh, Derry, why didn't you warn me?'

Her cousin was a smooth-faced man of thirty, his fine brown hair silky, cut in a fashionable style. There was quick intelligence in his face, but he had few scruples and his smile now was quizzical.

'I thought you knew! Father and son make the papers often enough, heaven knows, especially father, of course.'

International playboy, jet-setter, ruthless tycoon—

the labels were interchangeable and Mark Hammond lived up to them. Rachel had a fuzzy memory of his hard-pared face in grey newsprint, the self-willed arrogance of his eyes always recognisable.

Later, she had said, 'He won't come! He must have been kidding me. He won't turn up.'

'Want to bet?' Derry had had a cynical amusement in his smile.

'I hope to God he doesn't,' she had gasped.

'He fancies you rotten,' Derry had told her, laughing. 'Couldn't take his eyes off you! Like father, like son, remember. You could get a fistful of diamonds out of this, darling.'

Her face had gone dark red with anger and she had given Derry a killing look. 'Don't talk like that! You know me better.'

His hazel eyes had become wryly impatient. 'I wish I didn't,' he had muttered. 'This is a million-to-one-shot—don't blow it, baby. The boy is ready to go head over heels for you, and with his daddy's bank balance you could do very nicely out of it if you played your cards right.'

'Sometimes I could slap you!' She never took Derry seriously, but his cynicism hurt her.

He had taken her by the shoulders and spun her in front of the mirror. 'Take a good look,' he had said sharply. 'You have a sexy body, Ray. You even manage to look sexy in jeans, God help me. Use the advantages you have. What are you waiting for? True love?'

In the mirror her green eyes met his hazel ones. 'Just that,' she had said quietly and he had stared in grim silence.

He had pushed her away and stalked out, but that had not been the end of it. He had come back with fresh arguments again and again until she was sick of hearing about Nicky Hammond and his father's money.

Nicky had arrived spot on twelve. Rachel had opened the door to him in white jeans and a white T-shirt, her warm curved body tightly encased in them. Nicky had awkwardly handed her a large bunch of roses and she had found herself smiling at him, although she had been stiff with anger as she opened the door, on the point of asking him to go.

Derry had been all smiling hospitality, pouring drinks, offering nuts, but Nicky had barely removed his dazed eyes from her as she walked from the sitting-room to the kitchen. The hotpot had been a success and he had eaten it eagerly, filled with praise. Derry sat there, watching them with his shrewd, knowledge-able eyes, making her self-conscious and irritated. She was relieved when he had some excuse to leave, and from Nicky's brightening look she saw that the boy was pleased to be alone with her.

They had played records and talked. Nicky skirted around his family background and she did not ask him any questions. She discovered that he had been kicked out of his school for persistent truancy, that he was living with his grandmother in London and was sup-posed to be doing a course in business studies.

'I drop out whenever I can get away with it,' he admitted wryly. 'Olly never splits.'

'Olly?'

'My grandmother,' he explained, grinning. 'Olivia, but everyone calls her Olly. She's very small and very quick. Sometimes my father calls her Peanut. He says she's well salted and just one bite for anyone with good teeth.'

Rachel had eyed him curiously. 'Your father sounds rather sharp, himself.'

His face had clouded over. 'He's an absolute bastard,' he answered.

It had taken her breath away. In her world people did not refer to their parents like that.

He had looked up at her, his eyes' brilliant with hurt, and her words of reproof had died on her lips. It was at that moment that she had begun to feel really involved with Nicky, seeing him as a vulnerable, over-sensitive child with a peculiar vein of sophistication in his nature which he himself did not seem respons-ible for, as though he had received the imprint of a stronger, older mind into the yielding plastic of his character. He talked sometimes as though he were quite thirty, his words sardonic, flashing between un-certain youth and cynicism in a sentence, his very features altering, hardening.

She had changed the subject instinctively. That afternoon they had gone for a walk in the park and she had laughed at him as she swooped down the slide in the children's playground. A keeper yelled at her and she gave him a charming little smile, bringing a faint smile to his face as she walked away.

She fed the ducks while Nicky watched, then she had sent him off in a taxi while she went back to her flat. Derry had lifted a cynical brow. 'Changed your mind?'

'No,' she had snapped. 'Derry, I'm warning you— leave that boy alone. He's a nice kid. Step out of line and I'll walk out on you.'

He had looked taken aback. She had never threatened to leave him before and the threat impressed him with her sincerity.

It was a week before Nicky confessed his identity to her, his face uneasily flushed. She listened without expression, then she said quietly, 'I already knew, Nicky. Derry recognised you that first night.'

'Is that why you were so nice to me? Why you've let me come here and see you?' The words spilled out hotly, angrily, and she was sorry for the hurt behind them, the misery Nicky tried to hide behind his flushed young face.

'You must believe what you want to believe,' she had told him. 'We're all responsible for our own lives, Nicky. There are no locks on the door. Walk out and don't come back.'

Nicky had looked at her with hungry, hopeless eyes, making her ache with compassion. She had known what he was going to say before he said it and tried to stop him, her voice quick and urgent. 'Nicky, don't.'

It had been too late. He had had it burning at the back of his mind since the night he walked into her dressing-room and nothing could now stop him saying it.

'I love you.'

She had been wrung with confused emotions, blaming herself for allowing him to get to this stage, because she had known all along that the kindest thing to do was to chop him off before he got badly hurt. But her damnable sense of pity had got the better of her. People were always doing that, dragging one into an involvement one did not want, demanding more than one wished to give and leaving one with a bill one did

not want to pay, a total of bitter memories one could
not erase.

The sensible thing would have been to say goodbye
to him then and there. Instead she found herself mur-
muring anxiously, 'Oh, Nicky!' She had taken his
hand, held it tightly. 'I'm seven years too old for you
and we barely know each other. I'm proud that you
should like me, but it wouldn't do, Nicky. You must
see that.'

'Like you?' he had said with surprisingly adult
anger. 'I love you, Rachel!'

Their eyes had met and there had been fire in his
blue ones. She had bitten her lower lip, struggling for
expression. 'Nicky, you leave me with two choices.
Either you promise never to talk to me like this again,
or I stop seeing you.'

Nicky had gazed at her intently and seen that she
meant it, her face sober. 'I can't promise never to say
I love you again,' he had muttered slowly, 'but I'll try.'

The gravity with which he spoke had its effect, and
she found herself smiling at him. Already he had his
own place in her life, despite the gap between their
ages. She enjoyed having him around. Something in
him reached her.

'I'll be eighteen in two months,' he had said, when
she was silent. 'I come into quite a lot of money then,
Rachel. If you married me, you'd be able to stop singing in nightclubs. I'd give you everything you ever
wanted.'

'Everything, Nicky?' she had asked with a wry smile.
'Could you give me the sun, the moon and the stars?
I can get myself the black fur boots I want, the tabby
kitten, walks in the rain in London.'

The teasing had been gentle and he had taken the

point. 'Money doesn't mean much to you, does it, Rachel?'

'It means enough to eat, clothes, an occasional holiday and my own flat. I can get all I want by working, Nicky. I leave jet-setting and wild parties to those who think life is empty without them. The same goes for mink and diamonds.'

'You've read about my father?' Nicky's eyes were burning with emotions too confused to read. She thought she saw hatred, she knew she saw distaste, but did she see love there too?

She sat and listened then while he poured it out like a flood of tears, although his voice was always level and calm, but that was the measure of his climb to maturity, that now he could talk about his father without his voice breaking.

Mark Hammond, she discovered, was a man of thirty-nine. He had inherited a large firm from his own father when he was sixteen. 'He left school and went to work then,' Nicky told her. He grimaced. 'I can't imagine him as my age, but he was married when he was eighteen. My mother was the daughter of a millionaire. He married money. I was born when my father was twenty-one. I barely remember him from those days; I lived with my mother in New York and he lived in London. He flew over now and then, but their marriage was finished by the time I was old enough to know what was going on. I had a nanny. She would take me down to see my father and I would look at him and hate him. When I was eight, my mother died of pneumonia. My grandparents tried to keep me, but my father flew over and took me away with him. He sent me to school.'

The clipped words had a haunted ring, and Rachel

had looked at him with gentle thoughtfulness. 'You didn't like school?'

'Hated it.' Nicky barely parted his lips to say the words. 'I was American, remember. They kidded me all the time—bullied me, ragged me, made fun of me.'

'What about holidays?'

'I spent them with my father's mother ... Olly! They were the saving grace of my life then. She's just great.'

'You saw nothing of your father?'

'He arrived from time to time, with women in tow. I don't remember much about them except that they always made a big fuss of me, cooing over me and petting me, but even as a kid I knew it was all a big act.'

'And your father?' Rachel knew instinctively that here was the thorn embedded in Nicky's heart. His face changed every time he mentioned Mark Hammond, but she could not quite decide how much of hate and how much of reluctant admiration there was in him towards his father.

He had learnt to hide and disguise his emotions where Mark Hammond was concerned and she guessed that his passion for herself was a safety valve for the pent-up feelings he had never been able to show anyone else.

'He's the most ruthless man I ever met.' Nicky spoke with pathetic earnestness, frowning. 'I saw a Western once where there was a rattlesnake on a rock. They make a bloodcurdling noise before they strike. It reminded me of my father.'

She had made no comment, merely letting him talk, easing his mind by listening, since she saw that this was what he needed. The only other person he seemed to care for was Olly, his grandmother, and he could not speak of his father to her with any frankness.

After that session he stayed away for a few days and she suspected that it was because he was embarrassed by how much he had revealed to her, but he turned up again eventually, his glance shy and pleading. Derry gave her a malicious grin threaded with satisfaction. Rachel had sighed. Nicky was problem enough without Derry making it worse.

During the weeks succeeding that conversation they had seen each other almost daily. Nicky fitted himself into her life in an unobtrusive way. Sometimes he came to the club, but more often he arrived at her flat in the afternoon. At first she was sharp with him, since her afternoons were often spent in housework or shopping, but Nicky seemed happy just to trot along the shops with her, carrying her basket, discussing cuts of meat or the price of vegetables. His interest in the small routine tasks of her day touched her and made her wonder if the boy had badly missed sharing a mother's working day.

He loved to help her cook, weighing ingredients, vigorously stirring a saucepan or a bowl of cake mixture, afterwards childishly eating the remainder of the uncooked mixture. Rachel could remember herself as a child doing the same and smiled as she watched him. He was ready to dust or polish beside her, even prepared to clean windows.

It was a shock to her on her twenty-fifth birthday when he sheepishly handed her a blue leather case, his face flushed. Derry leaned over to watch her open it, avidity in his face.

Rachel's eyes flashed angrily as she stared at the diamond bracelet in the case. 'No, Nicky,' she said furiously. 'How could you think I would accept a present as expensive as that?'

'But it's your birthday,' Nicky had burst out, trembling a little. 'I wanted to give you something special!'

'I couldn't possibly let you give me something of this sort,' Rachel said with clipped precision. 'If you'd bought me a pair of gloves or a book I would have loved it, but not something like this!' She snapped the case shut and thrust it at him, her cheeks bright red.

Derry had removed the case from Nicky's hands and opened it, staring at the flash of the diamonds with glinting eyes. Rachel leant over and snatched it away, disliking the greed in her cousin's eyes. She pushed it back at Nicky. 'I'm insulted you should have thought I would take it!'

That had been three days ago and now she guessed that somehow the Hammond family had been apprised of Nicky's purchase and alarmed by it into investigating his private life. Perhaps the jeweller who sold it to him had rung up his grandmother and warned her. Nicky had a very large private allowance, he had told her. Even so, the withdrawal of such a sum to buy a diamond bracelet must have sent a tremor through the Hammonds.

Mark Hammond must have been summoned from the States. Nicky had told her that his father was over there for weeks, and she suspected the boy had not even known that his father was flying back. Possibly a private detective had followed the boy to the club. So Mark Hammond had come along to find out what sort of woman had his son in tow, and no doubt with that background, the older man had fixed ideas to start with. He must have an unrivalled knowledge of the sort of women young boys buy diamond bracelets for, Rachel thought drily.

Getting up, she dressed and walked out to find Derry lounging in the corridor, smoking beside the fire bucket. He gave her a wink. 'I saw Mark Hammond leave. That was quick. Did he threaten you with the Mafia or offer you money to leave his kid alone?'

She saw the eager brightness in his eyes and made a face at him. 'Neither.'

Derry's eyes narrowed. 'He didn't make a different offer, by any chance?'

She felt her skin colour and was furious with herself for betraying a reaction. 'Derry, that's enough!'

'You aren't going to clam up on me, baby?' He sounded plaintive, but there was sharp curiosity in his face.

'Mr Hammond didn't approve of my friendship with his son and he made that plain, that's all.'

'I bet,' said Derry. 'Nicky left with him and it looked to me as if the kid was in for a rough time with Daddy.'

Yes, Rachel could imagine that Mark Hammond would be cutting and cruel to the boy. She felt a twinge of deep pity for Nicky, but in a way it was a relief because now she need no longer feel any responsibility for him. No doubt Mark Hammond would whisk him away to the States. She wished she had told the man some home truths. All that Nicky really needed was a little of his father's time—but she somehow doubted if he would get it.

CHAPTER TWO

RACHEL was asleep when the flat door bell chimed. Yawning, she shrugged herself into her wrap and stumbled to the front door. When she saw Nicky outside she blinked at him, confused.

'Hallo ... what time is it?'

'Eight o'clock,' he said, and she did a double-take.

'What on earth are you doing here at this hour?'

'I have to talk to you. Can I come in?'

Derry appeared at his own door, his hair tumbled and his face bleary with sleep. Seeing Nicky, his eyes snapped open with interest. He raised a hand and vanished into his room again.

Rachel hesitated, then moved backward to allow Nicky to pass her. He walked into the sitting-room and she followed him when she had closed the front door. He stood in the centre of the room, his thin arms slightly too long for his blue sweater, his boyish body uneasily tense.

'What wrong, Nicky?' Rachel asked.

He pushed a long black curl back from his face. 'He saw you last night in the club, didn't he?'

She did not ask who he was talking about; they both knew. 'Yes,' she admitted.

'What did he say to you?' Nicky sounded hoarse, distraught. 'He insulted you, didn't he? Oh, Rachel, I'm sorry. I could kill him!'

She scrutinised him soberly. He looked as if he had

not been to bed all night, his features blurred with lack of sleep, his eyes slightly red around the lids.

'What have you been doing all night? Brooding? Did you have a row with your father?'

'He has a mind like a sewer!' Nicky couldn't look at her.

Rachel turned and walked through to the kitchen. 'Coffee?'

He followed. 'Please.'

She moved around the little room while he watched her, and there was a hot glitter in his blue eyes. Although he was hiding it she could feel new emotions in him and she bitterly guessed what ideas his father had put into his head. Nicky was impressionable, easy prey to a stronger mind, and he had a love-hate relationship with the barracuda who was his father.

'Why didn't you tell him there was nothing between us?' he asked her suddenly, not looking at her.

She got cream from the refrigerator and glanced at him wryly. 'He made me mad.'

There was a silence. Nicky was chewing his lower lip. 'He ... he said I hadn't offered you enough. Everyone has their price and I'd underestimated yours. He said I should have asked what you wanted instead of getting you the bracelet.'

'You know better than that, Nicky,' Rachel said quietly.

The black head lifted and the boy gave her a quick, uncertain look. 'Do I?'

She drew a sharp breath. 'If you don't, you'd better go now.'

His colour deepened. 'I'm sorry, Rachel! It's just that he sounded so sure.'

She felt anger coiled in her stomach. 'I bet he did! He has a one-track mind, but I thought better of you, Nicky, than to fall for it. You have to start being sure yourself. If you let other people's opinions sway you, you're lost.'

He watched her pour the coffee and add sugar and cream to his cup. She drank hers black as always, careful of her diet.

Huskily, Nicky said, 'I haven't changed, Rachel. I still love you.'

Rachel put down her cup and for a moment she was silent, then she gave him a warm, gentle smile. 'A whole month and you haven't changed your mind! Such fidelity, Nicky!'

His hurt look made her groan.

'Nicky, must we go over that again? Friends, yes, but there can never be anything more.'

'I've walked out!' He flung the words at her as if they had some relevance and the connection was dimly discernible. She looked at him with concern.

'How do you mean?'

'I sat up all night and then I climbed down the waterpipe.' He grinned at her. 'I did two weeks' climbing in Scotland with the school last year and I'm not bad. I went down that pipe like a monkey.'

'Why didn't you use the front door?' She was dry, amused by his dramatic instincts.

'He'd locked me in!' He sounded affronted and she could not blame him. He was nearly eighteen and Mark Hammond was treating him as though he were six, but then Nicky was heir to a large fortune, so perhaps his father's precautions were not too surprising, even if they were stupid.

'Why did he do that?' she asked, more in despair, than in expectation of an answer.

'I said I wanted to marry you,' Nicky muttered, head down, his ears burning.

Rachel stifled a laugh, biting her lip to make herself sound stern. 'Nicky! That was very naughty. You know there's no possibility of that. I'm far too old for you.'

'I know,' he said sulkily. 'When you're sixty I'll only be fifty-three ... big deal!'

Her laughter gurgled out, her green eyes dancing. 'I'm a phase you're going through, Nicky. You may not believe that now, but one day you will and then you'll be grateful to me.'

'I'd be grateful now if you'd let me make love to you,' he said, and she was stiff with anger.

'Nicky!'

He walked to the sink and stood with his back to her, banging his fist on the stainless steel. 'He made fun of me! He laughed. He said I hadn't a cat in hell's chance with you.'

Mark Hammond had walked all over his son with hobnailed boots, Rachel saw, and she felt irritation with the man. Nicky's wordless adoration had been touching. There had been no trace of sexuality in it. Now Mark Hammond had changed everything.

'What are you going to do now?' Rachel asked to distract him, and he turned and looked almost pleadingly at her.

'Could I stay here?'

She felt like laughing, but instead she gave him a direct look. 'Where do you think he'll look first?'

Nicky looked wildly around him. 'I won't go back— he's a swine. I'd rather walk the streets.'

She studied him and saw the weariness in his eyes with pity. 'You need some sleep,' she said. 'You can have my bedroom for a few hours. Derry won't get up until noon.' She hustled him down the corridor and into her bedroom, quickly straightened the bed and removed some clothes from her wardrobe. 'Don't worry. We'll sort something out when you've caught up on your sleep.' She left him and went into the bathroom.

After a quick, brisk shower Rachel was on the point of dressing when the bell chimed again. She pulled on her wrap and went down to the door. She was not surprised to see Mark Hammond standing there with a tight angry face.

Wordlessly she stepped back and waved him into the flat. She would not have been surprised to see a squad of strong-arm men with him, but he was alone.

He followed her into the kitchen. Gesturing to the coffee pot, she asked, 'Coffee? It is still hot.'

'Thanks.' He leaned against the wall, his broad shoulders now emphasised by a black leather jacket beneath which she could see a white roll-neck sweater.

'He's here, of course?'

Rachel poured the coffee. 'Cream? Sugar?'

'Neither,' he said tersely. 'Is he here?'

'Uh-huh,' she nodded coolly.

'Where is he?'

'In bed,' she said, and his eyes narrowed.

'Yours, of course.'

Anger and outrage made her voice brittle. 'Of course,' she said with a snap.

He put down his cup and pushed his hands into the pockets of his tight black jeans. For a man of his age, she thought, he was amazingly lithe, his muscular thighs moulded so tightly beneath the fabric of the jeans that he looked as if he had been poured into them.

'How long has he been here? All night?'

She glanced at the round white face of the kitchen clock. 'Half an hour, to be precise.'

His black brows rose. 'That's all?'

'That's all. He seemed worn out—he's been awake all night. I sent him to bed. There was no point in talking to a half-asleep kid.'

'You know, I suppose, that he wants to marry you?'

Her green eyes were cool. 'So he says.'

He nodded, his eyes on her face. 'All right, Miss Austen. How much?'

Rachel sipped her coffee, her eyes on the wall. She had a strong temptation raging inside her. She wanted to throw her cup at him. When she had herself under control, she said sweetly, 'I'm afraid I don't follow.'

He laughed, showing white teeth. 'Come off it!'

Lifting her eyes to his face, Rachel said blankly, 'I beg your pardon?'

'How much do you want to get out of my son's life?' he demanded.

'What makes you think I want to do anything of the kind?' Rachel asked.

His blue eyes slowly swept over her from head to toe, missing nothing on the way, lingering on the V-shaped lapels which folded back to reveal warm white flesh, the deep plunge between her rounded breasts.

'A woman of experience landed with an adolescent for a husband? I think not. How much do you want?'

She shook her head, not trusting herself to reply.

His mouth indented. 'Ten thousand,' he said flatly.

Rachel laughed.

He took a step, his face suddenly dark with angry blood. 'Women like you deserve to be whipped,' he said harshly. 'I'm too busy to haggle with you, Miss Austen. Twenty thousand and not a penny more.'

Her mind was spiralling in rage. 'Not a penny less than a hundred thousand,' she said, and had the satisfaction of knowing she had taken the breath from his lungs for a moment.

He stared at her with that hard, cold face and his eyes were blank. Anger slowly seeped into them, a fierce burning anger which made her nervous. Instinctively she took a step backward and he said through his teeth, 'You're quite right to be alarmed, Miss Austen. In my present mood I'd be willing to hang to get my hands round your pretty white neck.'

'Just stay where you are!' she said furiously.

He took an audible breath, his face tightening. 'Very well. I'll give you thirty thousand.'

'When Nicky's the heir to millions? Do you take me for a fool, Mr Hammond?' she mocked him.

'Yes, lady,' he retorted tersely. 'Only a greedy little fool would try to blackmail me. I could break you. I haven't even started on you yet. I was trying to arrange it the nice way. I expect Nicky to cost me money from time to time—there are always going to be women for a boy in his position and from experience I know women always cost money. But if you're going to be greedy I shall have to try other avenues.'

He walked to the door and Rachel followed him, but when he turned towards her room she slid past him, facing him. 'You're not waking the boy up when he has just got off to sleep. You've done enough harm for one night, Mr Hammond. Leave him alone!'

The sharp anger in her voice made his face change. He stared at her with narrowed, glittering eyes.

Derry's door opened and he looked at them. Mark Hammond stared at him, brows lifting steeply, and Derry gave him his charming smile, eyes faintly tentative.

The blue eyes swivelled to Rachel, a question in them.

'My cousin Derry Austen,' she said reluctantly.

Derry came down the corridor, held out a hand. Mark Hammond looked at it with distaste and ignored it 'Cousin?' he asked, and there was an unpleasant tone in his voice. 'He lives here with you?'

'Rachel is more of a sister to me,' Derry said with an easy smile.

'Yes?' The black brows underlined the mocking doubt in the voice. 'How long have you lived together?'

'Since I was eight years old,' Rachel said with a bite.

'Cosy.' Mark Hammond looked cynically at her. 'And no doubt Nicky swallowed that without hesitation?'

She moved back and opened the front door. 'Get out!'

He halted opposite her, put a long finger under her chin and lifted her face towards him, inspected it as if it were an object he was thinking of buying, his features satiric and distasteful. 'I'll be back.'

Rachel slammed the door behind him, and Derry whistled under his breath. 'What's going on? Where's the kid?'

'In bed asleep, I hope.'

Derry followed her glance down the hall and his face held triumphant amusement. 'He's in your room? And you told Daddy? What did he say?'

'Oh, do shut up, Derry,' she said wearily. 'I'm sick of the whole thing.'

He followed her to the bathroom, but she shut the door in his face. When she was dressed she came out to find him back in bed, his door shut. She went out shopping as usual and came back to find Derry up. He was in the kitchen whistling as he made himself some toast. He gave her a wink. 'The boy is still asleep—I looked in on him. He sleeps like a baby.'

'A clear conscience,' she said. 'You should try it.'

'Ouch. Baby, do I deserve that?'

'Yes,' Rachel said flatly. 'Derry, I've warned you. Stay out of this or I'll walk out.'

Derry threw up his hands. 'I know when I'm beaten.' He walked out with a little smile. She saw that the turn of events had amused him. Despite her refusal to encourage Nicky for the reasons Derry had kept pounding into her, the boy was here in their flat, sleeping in her bed, and Derry was heartened by that fact.

When Nicky drifted out of her room in his sweater and jeans he looked flushed and very young, sleep still giving his eyes a doped dullness.

Rachel scrambled some eggs and grilled some bacon for him. Derry had gone out and they were alone in the flat. Nicky yawned over his breakfast-lunch. 'I'm starving! Thanks for letting me sleep.'

'You're still growing,' she said, smiling. He appealed to the maternal streak in her, his gangling limbs and uneasy movements very touching. 'God knows how tall you'll end up. Are you the Incredible Hulk, by any chance?'

He grinned. 'Am I green?'

'You were when you arrived this morning,' Rachel said lightly.

He gave a chuckle. 'Maybe I am, then.'

She poured him some coffee, watching with impressed interest as the food vanished at enormous speed. He had quite an appetite. She picked at her own salad. When Nicky had finished his meal, she said, 'Your father called in, Nicky.'

He laid down his knife and fork and stared at her. 'What did he say?'

'Quite a bit,' she said drily, but did not fill in the details. 'I think you should go home, you know. You can't stay here.'

'Why not?' He looked at her through his lashes and for the first time she noticed their length and blackness, remembering with a curious little shiver that his father's lashes were very similar.

'You're going to be a very good-looking man, Nicky,' she said, smiling at him.

His eyes gleamed and he leaned closer, staring, 'Rachel?'

She drew back, startled. There had been a sudden maturity in his face, a force which bothered her, reminding her of his father.

'Legally you're under age,' she pointed out. 'Your father is your guardian and any court would insist that you go back. After all, he's right—we both know that. You have to go on with your studies and fit yourself for the world you're going to live in when you're grown up.'

He caught her wrist and drew her hand to his mouth, kissing the palm with a delicacy and passion which worried and surprised her.

'I'm grown up now, Rachel.'

'Please let me go, Nicky.'

The quiet tenor of her voice had its own effect. He reluctantly released her hand and she stood up.

'I'll ring for a taxi.'

'Don't bother,' said Nicky. 'I'll walk.' He looked at the blue sky beyond the window. 'It's a lovely day. I need the exercise.'

She walked with him to the door and he looked down at her, his eyes just above her own. 'Am I embarrassing you, Rachel?'

She felt a strong tenderness for him, the youthful lines of his face which would one day toughen into the same dark mask as his father's.

It was important that she should not hurt him. He was too vulnerable. She had it in her power to wound or elate him, and that power was a responsibility which she felt strongly. Never in her life before had she been conscious of such power to affect another human being. She looked at him with unconscious sweetness, her green eyes loving.

'You're so young, Nicky. If you were ten years older ...' She broke off, grimacing. 'That wasn't what I meant!'

'Wasn't it?' He cupped her face in his fine-boned hands, kissed her very lightly. 'Does age matter that much?'

'Oh, Nicky, you know it does. Can you imagine how people would look at me? Baby-snatching ... that's what they'd call it, and they'd be right. If the position were reversed it would be different. This is a man's world and men make the rules. Women just keep them. If I were seventeen and you were twenty-five, everyone would smile. You see what I mean?'

He looked longingly into her face. 'You don't find me boring?'

'Boring?' Her instant reply made his face light up. 'How can you think so?'

'My father said a woman of your age would find a seventeen-year-old boy boring.'

'It's time you stopped believing everything your father says,' Rachel told him. 'Just get back to your business studies and work until you drop, Nicky. That will show him. At the moment you're just playing around amusing yourself. It isn't any wonder he won't take you seriously.'

He listened, his face intent, then nodded. 'I'll try. I'll really try for you, Rachel.' He quickly kissed her again on the lips and shot away down the stairs. She closed the door and went back into her flat with a faint smile. He was a boy who needed to be guided rather than driven and his father had no idea how to manage him.

Mark Hammond was in the club that evening. Derry gave Rachel a strange little look as they both noticed him at the table he had sat at before, his cigar smoke a pale screen in front of his black head.

Rachel did not glance in his direction after that first quick look. Nicky was not out front tonight and she guessed that his father had locked him up again. The audience were enthusiastic tonight, listening intently to her and applauding with vigour. She had no illusions about her own voice. It was soft and slightly husky, but it would never make her a great star. The smoky slur of her accent had charm without being irresistible, but she was technically proficient and Derry played perfectly with her, his touch sure and competent.

She had barely closed her dressing-room door when it opened again. She was seated at the dressing-table, beginning to take off her make-up. In the mirror she met Mark Hammond's eyes.

'What do you want, Mr Hammond?'

'We've an unfinished business deal to put through,' he said in a derisive voice.

Rachel went on taking off her make-up, ignoring the way he watched her with those narrowed blue eyes.

'I've been talking to my son,' Mark Hammond went on.

'About time,' Rachel observed. He lifted one black eyebrow and she looked at him in the mirror. 'You should have talked to Nicky more often in the past.'

'I'm a busy man, Miss Austen. Nicky has had the best of care, believe me.'

'I don't believe you,' Rachel said.

He looked sharply at her. 'What?'

'Nicky has had the most expensive of care, but hardly the best. His grandmother obviously loves and cares for him, and Nicky loves her, but he's been left at school far too often. For a boy with such a moneyed background he's strangely deprived.'

His hard mouth tightened. 'I didn't come here for a discussion on how to bring up my son, Miss Austen. Shall we get down to business?'

'Since that's apparently all you understand, very well, Mr Hammond,' Rachel said brusquely.

'We'll make it short and sweet, shall we? A hundred thousand, you said?' He brought out a cheque book and she stared at him, her face tightening.

He was writing, his head bent, and a dozen impulses flashed through her head as she watched. She was bitterly angry as he stood up and handed her the cheque. Without a word, without even looking at it, she tore it up and dropped it, watching the white pieces flutter to the floor.

She heard Mark Hammond inhale sharply.

'The price doubled last night,' she told him, raising her eyes to his face.

He was black with rage, his blue eyes like steel chips, little flames flickering in them. 'You little tramp!' he ground out, then his hands came down on her shoulders in a vice-like grip, dragging her to her feet as helplessly as though she were a doll.

Rachel barely had time to realise what was happening before she was forced against his hard body, her hands crushed against his chest, his hand tangled in her rich chestnut hair. His fingers tugged painfully, yanking her head backward. His blue eyes glittered on her face, then his mouth was rammed down like a weapon against her lips, the bruising force he was using paralysing her. She was thoughtless, empty, merely passive for a moment, then realisation hit her and she began to struggle bitterly, pushing against his chest. She tried to speak, but the parting of her lips was a mistake. He took advantage of it at once, the hot exploration suffocating her.

Kicking and wriggling, she tried every way she knew to get away from him, but he was possessed of a strength she could not combat. The hand at her back, pushing her towards him, began to slide slowly down her body. She felt his thighs pressing against her own and was conscious of a flare of awareness inside herself, a double awareness, since she realised that Mark Hammond was as aroused as she was, the hardness of his body made her only too conscious of that.

She made herself go limp, her brain working clearly at last. He sensed the yielding and his hands moved more caressingly, one tunnelling beneath the heavy rich weight of her hair, the other moving up to stroke the warm bare skin above her dress.

Rachel wriggled her hands upwards and he allowed them to escape, drawing back slightly to look down at her through half-closed lids.

Freed, she gave him a push with all her strength and caught him off guard long enough to back, lifting a chair to keep him away as if she were a lion-tamer and he a savage beast.

'Stay where you are, Mr Hammond!'

He gave her a wry grin. 'I've no intention of pursuing you, Miss Austen! I've already learnt what I wanted to know.'

She warily lowered the chair but stayed where she was, staring at him. 'Which was?'

He shrugged. 'Forget it. You can forget the two hundred thousand, as well. You've had your chance and you blew it.'

She was sick of the entire business, so she came slowly back to her stool and sat down, her elbows leaning on the dressing-table. 'I don't want any of your beastly money. Get out and don't come back.'

He sat down where he had sat before. 'Will you have dinner with me, Miss Austen?'

Rachel was puzzled and wary as she looked at him in the mirror. 'Why?' she asked him bluntly.

'I suspect it's time we had a frank discussion about my son,' Mark Hammond murmured with a dry smile.

'It's time you had a frank discussion *with* your son,' Rachel retorted. 'Have you ever actually sat down and talked to the boy?'

The blue eyes were intent on her. 'What's your real interest in Nicky?'

She gave him a wry little smile, her green eyes self-derisive. 'I suppose I have a strong maternal streak.'

'Maternal?' Mark Hammond's brows shot up and he gave her an amused smile. 'Does Nicky know you regard him in that light?'

'If you tell him I'll cut your throat,' Rachel said forcefully. 'I've never met anyone who needed reassurance as much as your son does. He's desperately in need of someone to care for; someone to care for him.'

The broad shoulders were held tensely. 'He's crazy about you. And he doesn't see you in any motherly light, either. Don't kid me you think he does.'

She smiled, her green eyes tender. 'Poor Nicky, of course not, but then he's looking for a soulmate.'

'And you're looking for a son? An odd relationship.' The sardonic voice was biting.

'I'm not looking for anything,' Rachel snapped. She gave him a furious glare. 'Do you know, you're the most irritating man I've ever met. Every word you say seems to make my hair prickle on my head. Ever since you walked in to the club that night you've been drawing all the wrong assumptions about me.'

'Draw me a diagram of the right one,' said Mark

Hammond. 'You can do that over dinner. I've booked a table. I'll wait outside for you.'

He walked out and Rachel contemplated the closed door with distinct impatience. For a moment she just sat there, wondering if she was insane to even consider going out with him, then she finished taking off her make-up and changed.

When she joined Mark Hammond he was leaning on the wall in a lounging attitude, his eyes on her as she walked slowly towards him. The intimate flick of his blue eyes gave her the impression of being visually stripped by an expert. He looked as if he knew precisely what lay beneath her cream dress and there was dry appreciation in his hard face as she joined him.

He was inches taller than his son, his black hair ruffled and just faintly touched with silver in places, the threads shining in the glare of the electric lights. The hair had a slight wave to it as it fell to his collar, thick and glossy with a blue-black gleam to it. His dark suit was exclusively cut, the perfect unchanging fashion which went beyond fashion, his waist tightly held beneath the waistcoat, underlining the lithe body under it.

He slid her into his long steel-blue limousine. The cream upholstery had the pleasant scent of expensive leather. When he started the engine it purred so softly that she could distinctly hear the tick of the clock on the dashboard. He threw an oblique glance over her and gave her a brief, upward smile which held charm and male allure.

'Did I tell you that you looked very lovely in that dress?'

Rachel gave him a dry smile. 'No, and don't bother.

I'm sure your sexual weapons are potent, Mr Hammond, but there's no need to point them at me. I have no intention of marrying your son, or becoming his mistress, so you can ease your mind of those fears.'

'You still look lovely,' he said calmly, easing the clutch. The car softly moved away into the thick traffic and Rachel leaned back in the opulent passenger seat, enjoying the touch of luxury she was getting. She had a horrible suspicion she was going to regret this in the morning, but at this moment her heart was moving far too fast and she was deeply conscious of Mark Hammond's lean, muscled body beside her. It irked her to admit it even to herself, but she knew perfectly well that from the moment she met him she had been far too aware of him. He might anger, irritate, even infuriate, but he was a sexy, exciting man, and the fact that he was very wealthy meant absolutely nothing compared to the impact that dark head, those incisive blue eyes, that hard body had made on her pulses.

CHAPTER THREE

HE took her to a dimly lit restaurant in Mayfair. She recognised the name at once, but she had never been there before; it was way above her income bracket. From the moment she stepped inside the smoked glass doors she could sense the exclusivity, the luxury of both the surroundings and the clientele, and her nerves prickled irritably. Walking to the table at which they were to sit, she held her head high, refusing to allow the soignée women she passed to glimpse the inner uncertainty in her green eyes. Even so, she received a distinct impression of casual wealth from the cut and style of other women's clothes, the flash of jewellery, the enamelled perfection of the female faces.

Across the table, Mark Hammond ran a comprehensive eye over her and she met his stare head on, mouth tight. 'You're quite something, Miss Austen,' he said softly, to her surprise. Then he picked up the menu and began to study it with apparent concentration, leaving her feeling that he had lost interest in her.

When they had ordered she sipped the aperitif in front of her, nervously playing with the cutlery, her eyes on the gleaming white of the tablecloth.

'So,' Mark Hammond said suddenly. 'We discuss my son.'

Her head lifted, the light picking out golden strands among the warm mass of her hair. The creamy skin grew more flushed. 'Nicky is an odd mixture of child and man,' she told him seriously. 'You've neglected him for too long, Mr Hammond. You've hurt him. If he's turned to me for affection it's because you've never given him any.'

He gazed at her from beneath half-closed lids. 'I'm sure you've already fulfilled these needs of his, Miss Austen. Five years ago it might have been possible for me to reach the boy, but in the last few days I've realised that Nicky is grown up and what he wants is a woman, not a father.'

'You're wrong!' Rachel leaned forward to emphasise her point and the narrowed blue eyes dropped to the taut bodice stretched across her full breasts, slowly probing the low neckline of the dress.

Angrily she sat up again, clenching her hands into fists. 'Will you please take me seriously?'

A mocking smile touched his mouth. 'I'd be very glad to, Miss Austen,' he said softly, and her cheeks burned at the unhidden implication.

'For God's sake! Must you have such a one-track mind?'

'It's a track you seem to know very well,' Mark Hammond drawled with a lift of the dark brows.

Rachel abandoned caution, her temper flaring. 'Oh, I know all about men like you, yes—in my profession they're a permanent nuisance. You can get very sick of fighting off men who think a singer is easy prey, believe me. They never seem to get the message. Saying "hands-off" doesn't seem to work with them. All they really understand is a punch on the jaw—and you're going the right way to get one, Mr Hammond!'

He laughed outright at that, his manner relaxing.

Leaning over the table, he picked up one of her hands before she could snatch it out of the way and stared at it with his mouth curling in amusement. 'Do these soft little hands pack a punch? I don't believe it.'

'You'd better!' Her green eyes flashed a warning.

He released her hand and she sat far back, her hands curled in her lap. Mark Hammond lifted his glass and drank, his eyes on her flushed face.

'At a guess, I'd say that the fellow with the deterrent is your alleged cousin who lives with you.'

'Derry and I have always lived together,' she said shortly. 'There's nothing whatever between us of a romantic nature.'

'Nicky's jealous of him.' Mark Hammond watched her as he spoke, and she felt herself start in surprise.

'He's never shown it!'

'No?' The blue eyes glittered. 'What would you have done if he had? Would cousin Derry have been turfed out until you'd got Nicky to marry you?'

'I have no intention of marrying Nicky! I told you!'

'Have you told Nicky?'

Rachel said tightly, 'Yes! Frequently!'

'Yet he still thinks you will? You can't have been very convincing, Miss Austen.' He smiled with catlike malice. 'Perhaps you didn't try to be convincing?'

Their first course arrived and she busied herself with that, her head bent, ignoring him, since she was now so angry that she could have picked up the plate and flung it at him.

'You aren't touching your wine,' Mark Hammond drawled. 'Want to keep a clear head, Miss Austen?'

She defiantly picked up the glass and swallowed

half of the wine, furiously aware of his derisive grin.

'How did you come to meet Nicky?' he asked over their steak and salad.

She lifted her head. 'He just came into the club with some friends.' Retailing the incident of the noisy blonde girl she explained how Nicky had come round to apologise afterwards, and Mark Hammond's mouth twitched in dry amusement.

'How soon did you realise the sort of fish you'd hooked, I wonder?'

Rachel gave him a cold glance. 'My cousin recognised him on sight.' Her tone was cutting. 'I realise just what you'll make of that.'

He inclined his black head, his blue eyes narrowing. 'I make this of it, Miss Austen. You're a very clever woman. You've played Nicky with incredible skill; too bad you're not going to be able to land him.'

She pushed her plate away, preparing to rise. 'We really have nothing to say to each other. Goodnight.'

He half rose, clenching an iron grip around her wrist. 'Sit down!'

Surprised by the harsh tone, she unwillingly sank back into her chair. He released her and leaned back. 'Coffee?' he asked as coolly as though nothing had happened.

Over the coffee she made one final attempt to make him see the problem as she saw it. 'Nicky is lonely and unhappy,' she said seriously, her eyes on the hard face opposite. 'He needs affection. The best possible course you could take, Mr Hammond, is to take Nicky back to America with you when you go back. Introduce him to your firm. See something of him. Talk to him. That's what he needs—his father showing he cares for him, not just a stranger walking in and out of his life and ordering him around as if he were a puppet.'

He gave her no reply then, his face unreadable, the black brows drawn over the blue eyes in a deep frown. Summoning the waiter, he paid the bill and they left. He strode beside her, his long legs forcing her to walk fast if she wanted to keep up with him. Reaching his car, he put her into it and walked round to slide in beside her. He did not switch on the engine, merely turned to face her, his face watchful.

'You seriously suggest I take Nicky to the States with me?'

Rachel almost sighed with relief. 'Seriously,' she urged.

He put a hand out, taking her chin between cool fingers, tipping it back so that his blue eyes could probe her features.

'Are you in love with the boy?'

She felt her skin colour warmly and knew he saw it. 'Don't be absurd!'

'You seem very concerned about him.'

'I am concerned,' she said quickly. 'Nicky arouses a protective instinct. He's such a sensitive, vulnerable boy.'

'Not bad looking, either,' said the dry, cynical voice.

Pulling her chin out of his grip, Rachel said wryly, 'When he's a man he'll be devastating.'

There was a silence. She looked up and found Mark Hammond eyeing her with an odd expression. He started the engine and the car purred away from the kerb. His eyes brooded on the traffic, the lean body barely moving as he drove.

He drew up outside her flat and she nervously bit

her lower lip, 'Thank you for the meal.' Glancing at the car clock she saw that it was one in the morning. 'Heavens, look at the time! Goodnight, Mr Hammond!'

'Aren't you going to ask me in for coffee?' He sounded sardonic. 'Or would your "cousin" object?'

She flushed. 'It's very late.'

'Does Nicky stay late?'

'No, he doesn't! He never comes here after the show.' She met his disbelieving eyes angrily. 'Do you want to know what Nicky and I do when he spends an afternoon at my flat?'

His mouth crooked cynically. 'I can imagine.'

'Then you'd be wrong! He helps me with my housework, he does the shopping with me, he peels the vegetables and washes up! The big gap in his life is a mother, Mr Hammond.'

He laughed outright at that. 'God almighty, do you really expect me to swallow that? The boy wants to get into bed with you, not peel vegetables.' His eyes slid down over her. 'The only peeling he wants to do with you is to peel your clothes off.'

She slapped his face as the last words hit her. His head jerked back under the impact then he shot forward on a rebound and his hands grabbed her shoulders and shook her, leaving her dazed for a moment or two. When she recovered her senses she was in his arms, his mouth punitive, the forcible demand of his kiss violent. All her instincts clamoured for her to surrender to the surging passion which began to climb inside her, but she held herself tensely, pulling back, thrusting her hands against his wide shoulders.

He let her go, surveying her angry face with a

peculiarly empty expression. Without a word she was out of the car, slamming the door behind her. Unhurriedly she walked away and heard the car burst with a roar, then flash away down the street.

Derry was waiting up for her, a curious look on his face. She looked at him without speaking, her mouth compressed.

'Well?' he asked quickly.

'Well what?'

'Come off it, Ray. You know what I'm asking! What did Hammond offer you?'

She felt the hot sting of her mouth where Mark Hammond had kissed her and felt like screaming. 'A hundred thousand pounds,' she said with bitter sarcasm.

'A hundred thousand!' Derry pursed his lips and whistled very softly, his eyes brilliant.

'I tore up the cheque!' Rachel walked towards the bathroom and Derry followed hurriedly, his voice behind her trembling.

'You did what? Ray, are you insane? A hundred thousand? We could . . .'

'We?' She turned on her heel and looked at him so angrily that he fell back, grimacing. 'We could do nothing,' she snapped. 'I've told you often enough, but I'll tell you for the last time, Derry—I am not going to make money out of Nicky Hammond. I'm sick of your mercenary attitude to that boy. In fact, I think it's time we split, Derry. It's time I faced the fact that our childhood days are over and whatever we had in common as children died a long time ago.'

Derry pushed his hands into his pockets, his light hair shadowed, his eyes on her face. There was wry acceptance in his features.

'You're a strange girl, Ray.' He smiled suddenly at her, the old charm in his face. 'Strange but nice,' he added. 'Maybe you're right. I'll move out as soon as I find another place.'

'Thank you,' said Rachel, feeling ashamed of her outburst now, yet instinctively feeling that she had been right when she said that it was time they split up. When she first started work, it had been sense for her to live with Derry. He had been a very necessary protection for her for years. Since their surnames were the same, men often took him for her brother, and she encouraged them to do so, since it meant that they left her alone once they knew she had an able-bodied young man living in the flat with her. Their relationship had always been that of brother and sister, indeed. Derry's parents regarded her as their daughter and Derry had always treated her with brotherly affection.

'Tell me,' Derry asked quietly, 'what did Hammond say when you tore up his cheque?'

She made a self-mocking little face. 'I told him I wanted double the amount,' she admitted, her eyes wry.

Derry's eyebrows lifted in a quizzical grin. 'Did you now? I wonder what made you say that?' He watched her closely and she looked away, aware that she was blushing.

'He makes me so angry! He's the most cynical, nasty-minded swine I've ever met! He interprets everything in a black light.'

'Does he fancy you?' Derry asked so lightly that she was taken aback for a moment.

Her colour deepened. It was a question to which she could give no answer, although it was one she had been asking herself for some time now. Mark Hammond's kiss had been brutal, insulting, but she knew there had been aroused desire behind it. Without answering Derry she walked into the bathroom and leaned against the door, biting her lip.

Rachel had not reached the age of twenty-five without learning something about men and her own reactions to them. She had been madly in love at eighteen with a saxophone player she met in Glasgow. He had been a wickedly amusing man and their romance had only ended because Rachel discovered to her horror that he was married with three children. He had lied about that, and the experience had taught her to be wary of the men she met, refusing to hurry into any relationship until she was sure of her ground. Her professional life had meant that she moved around quite a lot. Her set-up with Derry had given her the background and protection she had needed at a difficult period of her life. Somehow she had come through the years since her first love affair without getting badly burned. Love had occasionally brushed past her, but it had never laid a mark on her. She was free of painful memories, but she was also very defensive, wary, inclined to draw back from the slightest hint of danger.

From first seeing Mark Hammond in the nightclub she had sensed the danger he represented. His formidable height and the width of his shoulders reinforced the fleshless strength of his features. A man might well think twice about challenging him; a woman would be wise to keep out of his path. There were too many danger signals in his appearance: that sensual mouth, the cynical lines around eye and mouth, the sardonic glint in the blue eyes. From what Nicky had told her of his father, Mark Hammond was a man who used women as ruthlessly as he manipulated his business acquaintances. Women were disposable chattels to him. He took what he wanted from them without counting the cost, either for himself in terms of cash or for them in terms of emotional stress.

His view of women was plain enough both from what he himself had said to her, and from what Nicky had repeated to her of his father's conversations.

Rachel's independence and integrity rebelled against such a man. She refused to be reduced by him to a toy for his idle hours. Yet she was irritably aware of something within herself which was flicked into life whenever she set eyes on Mark Hammond. The man attracted her.

She stripped and stepped under the shower, revolving beneath the warm jet, watching the soap wash off her limbs. It was an easy decision to make, she thought. She must avoid Mark Hammond like the plague.

Easy to think; another matter in practice.

Three days later Nicky arrived at the flat with shining eyes and a look of eager excitement. Derry was packing, having found himself a flat nearby. Rachel let Nicky into the sitting-room with a faint sigh. She had not seen him since her last encounter with his father and she had begun to hope that they had both flown off to the States. So although Mark Hammond had seemed impressed with her advice, he had not taken it? She repressed a feeling of anger. What had she expected? He was too selfish, too determined to have his own way.

'We're having a party,' Nicky burst out, giving her

a vivid smile. 'For me! Mark ...' He broke off with a
flush and a self-conscious look at her. 'My father asked
me to call him Mark, Rachel. He said I was too grown
up to use baby names.' He hurried on with that eager
voice, 'He wants me to go back to the States with him,
so as I'll be over there for my birthday he suggested
I have a birthday party for my friends before we leave.'

Her voice warm with pleasure in his obvious delight,
Rachel smiled at him. 'That sounds like fun!'

Nicky's blue eyes were fixed on her face and she
sensed that something more was coming. His eager excitement had more basis than the mere fact that he was
having a party for his birthday. 'Will you come,
Rachel?'

She drew a shaken breath, eyes widening. 'Me?'

'Please, you're the only one I really want there,'
Nicky muttered in a hurried fashion.

'Nicky, I can't,' she protested, biting her lip, regret-
ting that she must puncture the bright balloon of his
pleasure.

He looked at her as if she had hit him, his colour
draining. 'You must!' There was that hurt, disbelieving look in his eyes, the look she recognised and
dreaded since it was a potent weapon against her own
soft heart. Then his face lit up as if he had thought of
something which would alter her determination. 'Mark
wants you to come! He said I must invite you.' Seeing
the incredulity in her face, he added shyly, 'He wants
to thank you for being so kind to me.'

Rachel forced all expression out of her face, her
mind working hard and fast. She could imagine why
Mark Hammond wanted her to go to Nicky's party,
and it was not for any reason of gratitude or generos-

LOVE IS A FRENZY 53

ity. He would want her there only for one reason—to point up to her the vast gap between herself and Nicky, both in terms of the worlds they moved in and in terms of age. Nicky's school friends and peers would all be there, gay young people from a velvet-lined existence of which she knew nothing. She would be out of place and Mark Hammond meant both Nicky and herself to see it.

Still, he had apparently taken her advice about whisking Nicky off with him to the States. If he wanted to neutralise any further danger that Nicky would hanker after her, she could not blame him. It might, in fact, be the best plan, the kindest course, in the end. It would entail humiliation for herself, maybe, but that would not deter Mark Hammond and she must not let it deter her. It was for Nicky's sake.

She looked at him gently. 'Well, if you want me there, Nicky, I'll come.'

His eyes shone. 'That's great, Rachel!' He looked round. 'Of course, Derry must come.' His voice was reluctant and she sensed that he did not want Derry, but that his father had suggested Derry be invited, too. Mark Hammond, perhaps, wished his son to see her with Derry in an intimate party atmosphere, to point up the relationship which no doubt the father had been at pains to insist upon to Nicky.

'I'll tell him,' she promised. 'Are you getting on better with your father now?'

'He's quite human when you get to know him,' Nicky said with a casual tone which did not deceive her. 'He took me to a sauna yesterday.' His grin was impish. 'He strips better than I'd expected. I tell you what, Rachel, the old man's in quite good shape.'

Her lips twitched at the condescending, man-of-the-world intonation. 'Did you tell him that?'

Nicky looked aghast. 'You've got to be kidding! He'd flay me alive.'

'And have you for breakfast!' she laughed at him.

'You bet!' Nicky was grinning with delight. 'We've seen a show and been to the races. Mark only gambles for pleasure. If he loses, it ceases to be a pleasure and he stops.'

She could hear his father's voice behind every word, and she smiled at him. 'And so you're going to the States? That should be very exciting.'

'Mark wants me to start work soon—he says you don't learn a thing at these business courses. You learn by working at the job.' Nicky looked earnestly at her. 'I could have told him that. He was pretty understanding about my being bored at the college. He said I won't be bored when I'm doing the real thing. Work is like a woman—there's no sense in playing around, you just ...' He broke off, his face turning red. 'Oh, well, I forget the rest,' he said unconvincingly.

She could imagine the cynicism which had followed after those words, Rachel decided, but she gave no inkling of her irritation as she smiled at Nicky. Mark Hammond was infecting the boy with his own jaundiced view of her sex and she wished she could wipe the cynical smile off his face.

Nicky flew off soon afterwards. Mark, he confided, was taking him to buy some clothes. 'He says my tailor is lousy,' he explained with a happy grin. 'Mark is taking me to his! Mark isn't one of these stuffy old birds who wear pinstripes, Rachel, is he? I mean, he wears some fantastic gear, especially out of office hours.'

Every other sentence just had to contain the name Mark, Rachel thought, as she saw him off. Nicky was busy transferring his burning adoration from her to his father and, although she had known it was what he really needed, she was ludicrously envious. Nicky's eager emotions had been touching, flattering, ego-boosting. She only hoped Mark Hammond would deal gently with the boy.

When she told Derry about the party, his eyes narrowed and a gleam shot into them. 'You say Hammond *père* knows we're both invited?'

She nodded.

Derry frowned. 'Odd, that. I would have sworn ...' He broke off and she finished the sentence for him.

'You would have sworn that Mark Hammond would die rather let either of us over the threshold? So would I, but I have a theory about that.' She briskly gave him her view that Mark Hammond wanted to show Nicky how impossible it would be to fit her into his world. Derry looked rather unconvinced.

'Anyway, whatever his reasons, we're invited. At last we get a chance to sample the high life we all read about,' he smiled.

Rachel eyed him drily. 'Don't expect too much, Derry. It's just another party and I expect Mark Hammond will see to it that the other guests are teenagers, Nicky's friends. We'll stick out like sore thumbs among them.'

'Rich teeny-boppers go for older men,' Derry said lightly, a grin on his face.

'Derry! Please, don't do anything stupid!'

'Stupid?' He gazed innocently at her. 'What do you mean?' Without waiting for an answer he wandered out, and she wished vainly that he had not been invited. Derry in a mischievous mood could cause trouble, and trouble was the last thing she wanted at Mark Hammond's house.

When she and Derry arrived the party was already in full swing. They had been working and Rachel was tired, her body drained after a rather extended session since an act had not turned up and she had had to go on twice.

They had changed in their dressing-rooms. She was wearing her only expensive evening gown, a very simple white dress in silk jersey, pleated finely and outlining every curve of her body, the neckline hung from two pleated gold straps which crossed her slender shoulders. She wore her hair in a rich, loose mass, cloudy around her face. Derry was far more casual, in a dark blue velvet jacket which looked vaguely theatrical beside her classic simplicity, but his slim figure had charm, she admitted, eyeing him with foreboding.

It was Mark Hammond who welcomed them, pressing drinks into their hands. He was totally casual, in a black shirt and jeans, giving him the prowling broodiness of a panther, his shirt partially left open, a thick silver chain around his brown throat. The sight of him made Rachel flush uneasily, glancing down at her own party clothes, filled with horrified suspicion that she was overdressed. A hurried glance around the crowded room showed her that she was not as conspicuous as she had feared, however. The guests seemed to have come as they liked—some wore glossy, expensive clothes, others wore jeans and T-shirts, the mixture somehow perfectly compatible since they were all so young.

'Nicky is somewhere about,' Mark Hammond told her, following her eyes. Derry was already moving off, his eyes on one of the pretty girls who decorated the room. Rachel uneasily watched as her cousin advanced on the small, kittenish blonde whom she remembered suddenly from Nicky's first visit to the nightclub. A giggle came from the girl as Derry said something to her, and Rachel frowned.

'Does it bother you?'

She turned her head, puzzled by Mark Hammond's dry question. 'Does what bother me?'

'Seeing your "cousin" flirting with other girls?' His blue eyes held a cold glitter as he watched her flush.

'When they're teenagers, yes,' she said frankly, staring back at him. 'Derry can be pretty potent.'

'Can he, indeed?' Mark Hammond's tone was biting. He swung his eyes back to where Derry was dancing with the little blonde, their bodies moving apart in time to the solid beat of the reggae which was playing. 'God, what a racket!' He put a hand over her arm. 'You don't want to listen to this stuff, do you? Let's find somewhere quieter.'

She pulled her arm from his grip, her pulses already going mad under the cool touch of his fingers. 'I'm quite keen on reggae, actually.'

His eyes narrowed. 'In that case,' he drawled, removing her glass, 'Let's dance, shall we?'

A refusal was on her lips when Nicky suddenly charged up, very flushed and elated, looking attractively dishevelled in a new white suit and pale blue shirt which, like his father's, was open at the neck. His black hair was ruffled, his eyes very bright.

'Rachel!' Excitement made him bold. He seized her by the waist and kissed her, then, almost trembling, kissed her again quickly. 'Come and dance.'

Without a glance at Mark Hammond she let Nicky drag her away into the throng. The others cleared a space as Rachel laughingly demonstrated her skill, her slim, rounded body moving sexily under her clinging dress, her movements easy and perfectly attuned to the music.

She had danced with Nicky a number of times at the nightclub and they had an instinctive rapport. Without their bodies so much as brushing they danced around each other, smiling at each other, fitting together as if they had planned a routine. Nicky was slightly taller, his thin young body graceful as he moved to the music, and he was not taking his eyes off her. Excitement blazed in him like a neon light.

'Fantastic!' One of the other boys was beside her, eyeing her with admiration. 'Dance with me next?'

'Shove off, Drew!' Nicky turned a red face to him. 'Rachel's with me!'

'Can't she answer for herself?' The boy was burly, a belligerent young man a little older than Nicky, his neck pink, his ears slightly protruding.

Derry flicked her a wicked smile, winking. He was still with the little blonde and he was getting all her attention. Her eyes were as bright as stars and as avid as a hungry cat's.

Nicky had turned to face his rival, bristling. Rachel put a hand on his arm, feeling the tension in his undeveloped muscles. 'Hey, this is a party, dig?' She mocked him, using teenage language, and he grinned at her, relaxing. Giving the other boy a brief look, she said, 'I'm Nicky's guest, chum.'

He took it with good grace, strolling off with the

look of one who has won a fight, and Nicky glared after him. 'Bighead!'

They danced for some time until Rachel gave Nicky a groaning smile. 'I'm too old for this! I must sit this one out! Where do you get your energy? Don't tell me! Peanut butter and Coca-cola!' They were, she knew, his favourite snack and he grinned at her.

Mark Hammond was lounging against the wall, watching with impassive attention. He had been there throughout, although Rachel had avoided glancing in his direction. He moved as they wriggled out of the crush of cavorting bodies. 'I'll take care of Rachel, Nicky. Loren looks as if she would like to dance with you.'

Nicky looked hesitant, torn between a desire to stay with Rachel and a desire to get back into the over-heated throng. His brief look over his shoulder brought a hopeful look into the eyes of the girl Mark Hammond had indicated. She was a particularly pretty child, Rachel noted with amusement, her pink face untouched by cosmetics yet filled with glowing radiance. The straight black hair fell like silk around her perfect features.

'Yes, go and dance, Nicky,' she said, and he looked at her.

'See you later, then?'

'When I've recovered my stamina,' she said lightly. 'At the moment I'm dead on my feet.'

He laughed and moved off to where the black-haired girl waited, her charmingly simple blue dress exactly the shade of her huge eyes. 'Hi, doll,' Nicky greeted her, and began to dance.

Rachel turned from watching them to find Mark

Hammond staring at her unreadably.

'Look well together, don't they?' he asked, and it was a jibe, she heard the sardonic note.

'Why not? They're the same age. She's a very pretty girl, too.' Rachel walked away from him, head high.

She had intended to sit down on one of the chairs around the cleared room, but Mark Hammond came up beside her and steered her deftly through the wide double doors into the hall. The cessation of the noise as he closed the doors behind them was almost too blissful and she gave a deep sigh of relief. Her head had begun to throb in time to the music and she knew she was in for a vicious headache any minute.

'This way,' said Mark, propelling her across the wide hall and into a large room. He switched on the light and she stood there, looking around her with interest.

'My study,' he explained, walking over to a narrow, highly polished table. Lifting a decanter he poured whisky for them both. 'Tonic or soda?'

'I hate whisky,' she said, not even bothering to be polite since she was finding his presence well nigh intolerable.

'This is medicinal,' he told her, returning to push the glass into her reluctant hand. 'You look as if you need it.' He took her elbow lightly and urged her towards the black leather couch which occupied one side of the room. A wide leather-topped desk took up the other, its cleared surface only bearing a businesslike anglepoise lamp and a silver calendar clock.

Rachel leaned back on the couch, her fingers clasped around the glass. Mark Hammond sank down beside her, his arm snaking along behind her head. He tipped the contents of his glass down his throat. 'Drink your whisky!' It was a command and it aroused her temper.

She gave him an oblique, irritated look. 'I told you, I don't like it.'

He leaned over to put his glass on the floor. 'You've a stubborn nature, Miss Austen.'

If she imagined that that was the end of it she had under-estimated Mark Hammond. Suddenly his arm was clamped around her and the glass was at her lips. Over the rim their eyes met in conflict. His blue eyes sparkled and he said softly, 'Drink it.'

To her own irritation she found herself obediently drinking, her face very flushed. After a moment he withdrew the glass and placed it on the table. She moved to rise and he spun, catching her wrist.

'Mr Hammond,' Rachel said in clipped tones, 'you're irritating me!'

He gave her a lazy smile. 'Do you have to be told what you're doing to me?'

The look in his eyes made her tense. 'Can we go back to the party now, please?' she asked him drily.

'The party happens here,' he drawled with a derisive smile. His hand moved up her arm, the blue eyes running slowly, appreciatively over her, lingering on the quickening rise and fall of her breasts beneath the white silk.

She had become used to being stared at, but this man was an expert and although the appraisal was insulting it managed somehow to make her tremble as though the glance of the blue eyes was that of a lover.

She was having difficulty just breathing and that made her angry. Lifting her head in defiance, she tried to change the subject. 'I'm glad you're spending more time with Nicky. It's already making a difference in him.'

'Forget Nicky,' he said, his voice brusquely abrupt. His eyes were a deep, brilliant blue, narrowed on her face. His fingers tightened on her shoulder, propelling her forward. The black head moved downward and she stared helplessly at his mouth. It seemed to come closer at a snail's pace until she was shaking, her own lips lifted, waiting for the touch of it.

From the second when it finally closed on her, there was nothing but a whirlwind of confused sensation; her arms going round his neck, her body tilted while he kissed her, his mouth driving her crazy, sending wild signals along her nerve paths.

He sat down, pulling her with him, his hands given total licence to go where they chose, the gold plaited straps sliding off her shoulders. He kissed her throat and her head fell back, feeling his lips on her skin in an intimacy she could make no effort to halt. It was the first time she had ever allowed any man to go so far, and the breathtaking sweetness he was arousing in her left her dazed.

The descent of his mouth between her valleyed breasts brought soft moaning from her. She lay across his lap shuddering, putting a hand to the black head, stroking his hair, feeling an intolerable need to show him tenderness.

He lifted his head at last and looked into her flushed face as she reluctantly opened her eyes, the lights dazzling her.

His finger touched her hot cheek. 'You're a very desirable woman,' he whispered. 'But you know that, don't you, Rachel?'

She gave him a confused, bewildered look, still dazed by his assault on her unawakened senses. His dark head was poised above her in hard outline, the sexy mouth hard with arrogance and satisfaction. The dominating movements of it on her had left her shaken to her depths, given her a hunger which appalled her.

Humour lit his eyes. 'You look drunk,' he said, his mouth curving with amusement.

'I feel it,' she breathed, surprised to hear her own voice.

He grinned at her. 'I'm flattered. You had the same sort of effect on me.'

Rachel gave him an ironic little smile. 'That I don't believe.'

His head dropped and his lips grazed a path over her skin, leaving heat wherever they touched. 'My dear, you're devastating, and I can't believe I'm the first man to tell you so.'

He was the first man since she was eighteen who had ever had this sort of effect on her, but she was not going to tell him that. She looked into the hard, sophisticated face and knew she was way out of her depth with him. He had already had a catastrophic effect on her senses. She had to guard against his impact on her heart.

She was off his lap before he knew she meant to move. The blue eyes surveyed her, catching her wrist before she could move to the door. 'Where do you think you're going?'

'Back to the party,' Rachel retorted.

'Oh, no, you don't,' Mark drawled, rising to stand beside her. 'I've no time to waste on games, Miss Austen. I'm not the sort of man who likes chasing his women before he enjoys them.'

The heat he had induced left her body. She was suddenly chilled. Even her lips felt bloodless. The derisive words had been so insulting that she made a wild gesture towards him with her free hand, meaning to slap him.

He caught her wrist, holding both of them, his fingers digging into her. 'What the hell do you think you're doing?'

Jerkily she struggled to free herself. 'I'm not for sale, Mr Hammond,' she said angrily. 'There's no price tag. Will you let me go?'

He stared into her face for a moment, eyes penetrating, then his hands dropped away and she turned and stumbled out of the room. She could not return to the party in her present mood. Running out of the hall, she escaped into the cold, clean night, her lungs drawing down air with sick relief.

CHAPTER FOUR

SHE should have known, of course, that Mark Hammond was not easy to shake off; he was like a bulldog once he had his teeth fixed in something, and he had made up his mind about her. He was at his table in the Harem the following night, smoking his inevitable cigar, his eyes narrowed on her through the smoke, the hard lithe body leaning back as he watched her act.

It surprised her, however, to see that Nicky was with him. Derry threw her an enquiring look, taking in Nicky's presence, one brow flickering in dry amusement. Derry had asked her earlier why she had left the party so suddenly and without saying goodnight to anyone. 'Our Nicky was quite distraught!' His eyes watched her as he added: 'He had a sneaking suspicion his dear daddy had made a pass at you!'

She had not answered, her face carefully blank, her hand steady as she applied make-up. After a moment she said calmly, 'I had a headache.'

Derry grinned, quite unconvinced. 'Yeah,' he said, leaving.

When they had finished their act tonight, Nicky hurried over to signal to them, his eyes pleading for her to join him and his father at their table.

Reluctantly, Rachel agreed and followed him through the couples now dancing to vigorous disco beat to where Mark was sitting. He half rose, giving her a sardonic little bow. 'Miss Austen! You sang very well tonight. A man could get addicted to that husky little voice of yours.'

She gave him a cool smile. 'Thank you.' Taking the chair Nicky pulled out for her, she smiled up at him and Nicky asked her what she wanted to drink.

'Martini,' she said. 'Thank you, Nicky.'

He glanced around helplessly for a waiter. The room was packed tonight and the dancing obscured the bar. Mark made no attempt to help, his eyes on the closely weaving couples in the middle of the room. 'I suppose I'll have to go and get the drinks,' Nicky groaned. 'Whisky, Mark?' The pride with which he said his father's name made her feel weak with compassion, and with dread. She had been responsible for the boy's transference of his adoration to this cynical, ruthless man. She should have known better. Nicky could get very hurt. His affectionate, sensitive nature could be ruined if he took every word, every look of his father's for gospel. He was too young to mimic Mark's hard, selfish cynicism.

When Nicky had gone, Mark slowly turned his eyes to her and they stared at each other in silence. 'I've a proposition to put to you,' he said, and her face tightened.

'You had my answer last night! I meant every word of what I said then. Please don't ask again.'

He gave her a cool little smile. 'You haven't heard what I want from you, yet. Just listen, please.' His face and tone had a quiet authority now. 'Nicky's grandmother would like to meet you.'

She was surprised, her eyes opening wide. 'She knows about me?'

He grinned suddenly, startling her further, because

there was an almost boyish charm in his hard face. 'Who do you think cabled me to fly over?'

Rachel grimaced. 'How did she find out?'

'Nicky's bank manager alerted her. The boy has a pretty big bank balance and we haven't placed any limit on what he draws out.' He had a sober expression as he talked. 'Despite your low opinion of me as a father, I do understand something about young boys. I wanted Nicky to learn the value of money. I gave him a generous monthly allowance and sat back to watch what he did with it. He did very well.' The wide shoulders shrugged. 'He has no extravagant tastes so far. The withdrawals were regular, careful. I was pleased. But of course when a very large sum was suddenly withdrawn the bank manager was on to it.'

'I can imagine,' she said drily.

Mark's eyes smiled, making her pulses leap abruptly. 'Exactly. I had a private detective on it within twelve hours. By the time I got here, we knew about you.'

'And drew obvious conclusions.'

He shrugged. 'My dear girl, what do you expect? When a boy of that age hands out extravagant presents to a nightclub singer it looks pretty open and shut.'

'Especially to a man like you.' Rachel made no attempt to hide her cold anger, her green eyes shining like pack ice.

Mark Hammond watched her, his hard mouth level. 'Actually, it was Olly who was excited—she was convinced you were a gold-digger who had her precious boy in her toils. She wanted me to tear Nicky away at once and rush off with him to the safety of New York.'

'That sounds like sense.' Rachel glanced at him. 'Why didn't you just do that?'

'I never act hastily,' Mark drawled. 'I wanted to take a good look at the sort of woman who had caught Nicky. After all, he's still very young. It might easily have happened again in New York. I had to know if he was a fool about women.'

She might have known that there was cold calculation behind it, Rachel thought. 'You wanted to assess his taste?' She put wry derision into the question.

'Precisely,' said Mark with a flick of one dark brow. 'When I deal with a man I like to know everything there is to know about his weaknesses and his strengths. If Nicky had fallen for a harpy with an adding machine for a heart I wanted to know about it, to be prepared for it happening again. I've always found that there's a repeating pattern in a man's relationships with women. They go for certain types. I had to know the type Nicky found irresistible.'

Before Rachel could answer Nicky was moving towards them, carefully carrying the drinks, his thin face concentrated. She gave him a quick, affectionate glance, her mouth softening. How young and serious he looked, his face all tension.

Glancing back, she found Mark Hammond watching her through half-closed lids, his features enigmatic, and colour flared in her cheeks at something in his blue eyes. What on earth was he thinking?

Nicky reached their table without spilling a drop and put the glasses down with a triumphant sigh. She laughed and he stood beside her, his eyes on her warm face. They exchanged a long grin.

'Just as you like it,' said Nicky. 'Dry with lots of lemonade.'

'Thank you, Nicky.' She picked up the glass and sipped. 'Mmm ... fantastic!'

LOVE IS A FRENZY

Nicky sat down beside her and put his elbows on the table, the thin wrists shooting from his cuffs. Propping his head on his hands, he gazed at her. 'Has Mark asked you? Are you coming?'

She looked across at his father. The hard face was impassive. 'I haven't asked yet,' said Mark. 'Why don't you ask her, Nicky?'

Eagerly, Nicky said, 'We've decided to go to Ambreys for a week before we fly to the States, Rachel. Will you come too?' He saw the movement of refusal in her surprised face and rushed on pleadingly: 'Please come! We want you, don't we, Mark? Olly wants to meet you and we can have a lot of fun.'

Rachel knew about Ambreys. Nicky had told her about it—the fabulous country house in Wiltshire which his father owned but rarely visited. Nicky had enthused about the creamy stone of the old house, the peacocks on the lawns, the gardens which were meticulously kept to a state of perfection for an owner who rarely saw them, the stables in which Nicky's palomino lived, a horse he only saw a few times a year but which he seemed to adore. She had thought then that such possessions were almost criminal—to own such lovely things and see them so infrequently was unforgivable.

'Nicky wants to see Ambreys before we go away,' Mark explained, watching her expressive face.

'Thank you for inviting me,' Rachel told Nicky. 'But I have a contract with the Harem, you see. I couldn't break it.'

'I'll sort that out.' Mark's crisp voice held a ring of certainty, the infuriating conviction that money solved everything. She gave him a cold look.

'I'm sorry,' she said to Nicky, shaking her head. 'I can't.' She rose and Mark's hand shot out to catch her wrist. She pulled, and it tightened around her like a steel bracelet. Her green eyes flashed angrily at him.

'I'll arrange for you to have a week's holiday,' he informed her levelly. 'We leave tomorrow. The Harem can have a guest singer for the week you're away.'

'They may not like that!'

He smiled sardonically. 'I do own the damned place.'

She looked down into his eyes with a desire to hit him and he read her expression without difficulty, his lips twitching as though she was amusing him.

'Please come, Rachel,' Nicky begged, his face disturbed as he watched them. 'I want to show you how beautiful Ambreys is—I know you'd like it. We'll have a marvellous time, I know we will.'

She was tempted, partly by a natural desire to see the lovely place Nicky had talked about with such affection, and partly by a bitter craving to spend a week with Mark Hammond. She was perfectly aware of the danger that he represented to her, but her willpower seemed to be weakening.

She glanced into his watchful face and then looked at Nicky. He gazed at her, his thin body tense, his eyes filled with pleading.

'All right, Nicky,' she said with a sigh.

He gave a whoop of delight, his smile lighting up radiantly.

She moved, her slim body curved beneath the glittering emerald green dress she wore, the heavy material falling to her feet, slits at the side from thigh to foot giving glimpses of white skin. 'I must go and change.'

'I'll drive you home,' said Mark Hammond, rising.

Nicky looked pleased, delighted with the way his

father seemed now to be accepting his relationship with Rachel.

She looked at them standing side by side, Nicky a young echo of his father, his face so sensitive and fine-boned, lacking the hard angular strength of Mark's features.

A peculiar tremor ran through her. A dark shadow seemed to swoop down over her eyes. These two ... boy and man ... seemed a predestined part of her, their impact on her already so deep she could not guess at the profundity of it.

She went to her dressing-room and stood, shivering, her face in her hands. She felt feverish as though she were ill. Why had she been so foolish as to agree to go with them to Ambreys? All her instincts warned her against it. She did not want to become even more deeply involved with the Hammonds. She could already foresee the tearing of an anguish which she feared.

Pulling herself together, she changed into the jeans and sweater she had worn on her way to the club. Slipping into her dark brown suede jacket, she opened the door. Derry had already gone, the manager told her, meeting her outside. 'Mr Hammond spoke to me about a week off for you,' he went on, somewhat drily, his eyes on her curious. 'It's okay with me.'

'Thanks.' She was curt, tense at the swiftness with which Mark Hammond had moved.

He was waiting outside for her. Nicky sat in the back of the limousine, his face close to the window, watching for her. His father stood on the pavement, hands in pockets, his lithe body poised with hard arrogance beneath his well-cut suit, his jacket drawn back by his posture revealing the tight-waisted waist-coat. Rachel walked towards him unwillingly, seeing the long, flat stomach and lean hips, then looked up suddenly into his dark face.

He took her arm and led her round the car, seated her beside him. She sensed Nicky's movement of protest and glanced over to smile at him.

While his father was walking round the bonnet, he leaned forward to say jealously, 'Why didn't you sit back here with me, Rachel?'

The car door opened and he sank back. Mark Hammond, moving into the driver's seat, gave the boy a quick oblique look. She saw the secret movement of that hard mouth, the hidden amusement.

He was making points. He knew precisely what he was doing, that calculating mind quick and shrewd.

He slid away from the kerb without speaking, and Nicky looked up in protest again as the car purred along familiar streets. 'Where are you going, Mark? We're dropping Rachel.'

'Your bedtime is well past,' Mark said without looking round. 'I'll drop you first.'

Nicky's face grew sulky. Rachel stared ahead at the brightly lit streets, emptying now of people.

When the car pulled up outside the Hammond house Nicky dived forward without warning and brushed a kiss along her cheekbone. 'Goodnight, Rachel.' He leapt out of the car and tore up the steps. Mark gave her a hard stare as he started the car again, but he made no other comment.

He was silent as they drove to her flat. When he had stopped the car outside the building he turned towards her, his hand on her arm preventing her from getting out.

'That isn't the first time I've seen Nicky kiss you. Exactly how far do you let him go?'

Her skin flushed angrily. 'What did you want me to do? Slap his face just now?'

'A clever woman like you could make him keep his distance without resorting to a slapped face.' The blue eyes held a sharp glitter. 'You managed it with me well enough.'

'Nicky's vulnerable, you're not. It would take a bull-dozer to knock you down, Mr Hammond.'

He grinned suddenly, his face filled with a charm which took her breath away. 'You can be a little shrew, can't you?'

Their eyes held and hers were the first to move away. 'I must go in,' she said huskily.

'Why did you run out on me at the party?' Mark asked, his eyes intent.

'I don't go in for bedroom games.' She looked at him coldly.

His fingers touched her face gently. 'Very well, Rachel, I apologise for speaking to you the way I did.'

'So you insult me grossly but I must be resigned to it, must I?' She pushed his exploring hand away from her hot face. 'Mr Hammond, you make me very angry!'

'My methods aren't always very admirable,' Mark admitted. 'When you're in a temper your eyes look like green glass.'

'What did you think my "other motives" might be?'

'Who knows? You could fancy Nicky ...'

'Oh, please!' She was so furious she could have hit him. 'He's a boy seven years my junior!'

'But you care a hell of a lot what happens to him.'

'Somebody has to!'

'Why should it be you, though?'

She glared at him. 'Because he cares for me—that makes him partially my responsibility. I can't just turn my back on a kid his age. I worry about him.'

'I've noticed.' He sounded very dry.

'I know perfectly well you've noticed. You see everything.' She was almost weary, her feelings too strong for her. 'I'm still close enough to my own adolescence to remember very clearly what it felt like to be that age and alone.'

'You had your loving cousin, surely?' He was mocking her, his eyes watchfully narrowed. 'I thought you'd lived with him since you were eight? What happened to your parents?'

'They died.' Her mouth barely parted to snap it out.

He settled back, his shoulders against the seat. 'Tell me about them.'

'There's nothing to tell.' She turned to open the door. Mark Hammond leaned over to hold her hand, forcing her to relinquish her grip on the door catch.

'I want to talk to you.'

Rachel turned her head, the thick brown cloud of her hair flicking against his face. 'Please! I have to go in now.'

'I gather your cousin has moved out. Why?' Mark's eyes were a few inches from her own, the dark pupils rayed with blue. Looking into them was a dizzying experience. At such close quarters the fragrance of his aftershave, the hard, lithe body pressing against her own, made her head spin.

'We quarrelled,' Rachel answered shortly, trying to control the odd swimming sensation in her head.

'About Nicky?'

'So clever, Mr Hammond,' Rachel mocked angrily.

He smiled and her heart distinctly missed a beat. So much for her belief that such clichés were made up from moonshine! She was angry with herself, yet the quickening rhythm of her heartbeat had been quite definitely interrupted for one second, so that its resumption seemed like a drum to her own ears, beating fast and hard.

'He's an opportunist, your cousin, something of a maverick, not very trustworthy, and he owes quite a bit of money. Gambles, drinks and chases women.'

'You'd know all about that!'

He looked amused. 'Would I now? What do you think you know about me?'

'What I read in the papers. It's enough.' Rachel lowered her lashes so that the green of her eyes only just gleamed through them. 'More than enough.'

'If you believe a word you read in newspapers you're naïve, Miss Austen. They prefer a glamorous lie to the truth, however solid.'

She lifted her eyes, smiling coldly. 'And are they all lies—the stories about you? The women, the parties, the jet-setting? Do you expect me to believe that after the way you've consistently behaved towards me?'

'You?' Mark's face held mockery. 'Shall we analyse that? I've made love to you, Miss Austen.'

Her face took on a hectic colour, her eyes angrily bright.

He was laughing at her. The wicked amusement in eyes and smile was maddening, but as he continued to speak her anger grew like a forest fire.

'And I got a very encouraging response, didn't I?'

She sat up, thrusting him out of the way. 'Oh, shut

up, you sneering swine!' She opened the door and wriggled out of the car, but as she made a dash for it towards her flat Mark Hammond stepped between her and the front door, his arm barring her path.

'I was making a point,' he murmured drily.

'Will you get out of my way?'

Patiently he said, 'My point was that I can't remember having to use force to get you into my arms, or to keep you there. Whatever you think my behaviour proved about me, Miss Austen, goes for you, too. Am I to leap to the conclusion that you're available because you let me kiss you at Nicky's party?'

'No! I told you that once!'

'Actions speak louder than words,' he said derisively.

She faced him, the night wind whipping her hair into a ruffle of dark strands.

He was silent, staring at her angry face, then he smiled with a wry admission. 'Miss Austen, what I'm trying to say to you is this . . . can we start again? Wipe out the last few encounters? I'm beginning to believe I was wrong about you. Can you accept that you could be wrong about me?'

She pushed the tangle of hair out of her eyes. 'It really doesn't matter, does it? We have nothing to say to each other.'

'Perhaps not,' Mark shrugged. 'But while you're a guest in my house it would be preferable if you were at least on speaking terms with me. Nicky would enjoy this week with you much more.'

It made sense, but Rachel did not trust this man an inch. After a little silence she sighed wearily, 'Oh, why not?'

'Have we a peace treaty, Miss Austen?'

She nodded, and he watched her as if curious about her thought processes, his eyes thoughtful.

'I'll pick you up here at nine tomorrow morning, then, Rachel.'

The use of her first name was deliberate, faintly underlined, his eyes watching her reaction to it.

She desperately wanted to get away from him. 'Very well,' she said, looking pointedly at his barring arm.

'Goodnight, Rachel.'

The arm still did not drop. She looked up at his face. He had a mischievous look. 'The name is Mark,' he said softly.

'All the world knows that!' Rachel was sardonic. 'Particularly the female half.'

'Of which you're one,' he pointed out, grinning.

She saw he would not move until she had surrendered. 'Goodnight, Mark,' she said drily.

His arm dropped and he looked amused. Hurriedly she walked past and escaped him.

She rang Derry before she went to bed. His reaction puzzled her. She had anticipated triumph, avid questioning about her week at the Hammonds' country house, but Derry seemed preoccupied with some matters of his own. 'Right,' he said. 'Have a good time.' When she had rung off Rachel sat frowning, wondering what he was up to, and whether there was trouble ahead. You never knew with Derry. He had a selfish, callous streak beneath that easy charm of his.

When his parents had caught some tropical disease during a holiday in Malaysia three years earlier, Derry had been all concern on the surface, but she had been shocked when she found a sheet of paper covered with scribbled figures and notes, revealing that he had

secretly been making a list of his parents' assets. Such
mercenary feelings when his mother and father were
seriously ill had shocked her. Their recovery seemed to
delight him, but she had been shaken for some time
afterwards.

Next morning she was up early, packing, and when
Mark Hammond called for her she was waiting for
him, decorously fashionable in a two-piece cord suit,
the deep brown shade picking out the highlights in
her chestnut hair.

Mark's eyes flashed over her without pause. 'Charming,' he said as he took her case and waved her ahead.

They drove fast through the crowded London sub-
urbs until they had reached the motorway, when the
sleek car shot off like a bullet from a gun. Rachel was
in the front of the car again, a fact which had not im-
mediately occurred to her until she saw Nicky's sulky
face. He was heavy-eyed this morning.

'A late night?' she asked him with a smile, turning
to speak to him.

He nodded, flushing a little. Mark gave her an
oblique little smile without saying anything, and she
guessed that the boy had been too excited to sleep.

They halted half-way for coffee. Mark coolly sent
Nicky to get it from the counter at the motorway café
at which they had stopped. Nicky went, but his backward glance was eloquent, and Rachel looked at his
father with sudden narrow-eyed suspicion.

Was he deliberately pairing off with her in this way
in order to push home to his son the fact that she was
much more in Mark's age group than in Nicky's?

Mark met her look expressionlessly, giving her no
help there. It was May and the sky was a clear, burning

blue, the air warm and fresh. Beyond the café window the green downland rolled onwards towards a smooth horizon.

'Were your parents killed in an accident?' Mark asked her out of the blue.

She nodded. Someone put a coin into a jukebox and the melancholy wail of blues music hit the air. Mark turned an irritated head in that direction, frowning.

'A traumatic shock to an eight-year-old,' he said thoughtfully, turning his head back suddenly.

'I got over it,' said Rachel. 'Derry's parents were marvellous to me. Children get over these things.'

'It sometimes goes so deep that one needs a psychiatrist to reach the problem,' Mark remarked, and she sensed that he was talking about Nicky. Their eyes fused. Her heart did it again. My God, she thought, what's wrong with me? That abrupt cessation of the beat was terrifying. The resumption was like a thudding hammer, leaving her weak and breathless.

'Nicky worshipped his mother,' Mark told her, and the quietness of the tone was a relief because she was beginning to be afraid he was aware of the calamitous effect he was having on her heartbeat. 'I was almost a stranger to him. I hadn't expected my wife's death. When it happened I flew over to get Nicky, and there was a tussle with my wife's parents. Unluckily the boy knew all about that and he resented the fact that I won. He wanted to stay with them.'

'Why didn't you leave him in the States? You've spent so much of your time over there since that it would have been common sense, surely?'

Mark's mouth twisted. 'I had a sentimental reason at the time—I thought he needed constant female care.

My mother, as you'll see, is very good with him. My wife's mother was a rather intense woman, a bit neurotic, and her daughter's death increased her tendency. I wanted Nicky to get out of that hothouse atmosphere.'

It sounded reasonable. She had heard Nicky's side of it; now she was hearing his father's view. They clashed in interpretation, but not in the facts.

Nicky arrived with the coffee. He had bought some crisps too. Mark gave them a wry look, refusing them. Rachel accepted some and Mark gave her a grim smile.

'Do me a favour—eat them quietly. I've a bit of a headache.'

Munching solidly, Nicky asked with a teasing grin, 'Too much whisky, Mark?'

His father clenched his fist playfully and offered to punch him in the jaw.

'You can't eat crisps quietly,' Rachel said with a defiant look.

'Right,' said Nicky, pushing some into his mouth.

Mark drained his coffee and got up. 'I'll see you two in the car,' he said as if they were children.

When he had gone Nicky turned to her with questioning eyes. 'What do you think of Mark?'

The engaging blatancy of the question amused her. 'I think he's exactly what you described,' she said, teasing.

'Come on, Rachel!'

She tousled his black hair fondly. 'Do you want me to praise him or bury him?'

He grinned. 'He ...' The husky voice broke off, then resumed. 'He likes you.'

Rachel looked at him gravely then, guessing at the

emotions behind his attempt at a calm face.

'Well, that's nice,' she said gently. Nicky's eyes held jealousy, confusion, uneasiness and the old bright adoration. He was becoming torn between his feelings for her and his new feelings for the man who he had always resented and now found so wonderful.

He was exactly the age to find Mark's sophistication and cynicism appealing, to imitate it without thought. Rachel hoped he would not form the same dark image of the world which Mark Hammond projected. Nicky was too young to be a cynic.

'You're very like your father,' she told him, and Nicky's eyes lit up.

'Do you think so?'

'A mirror would tell you as much,' she said, her face serious. Mark Hammond had taken a risk with her, she thought. He had treated her as if she were a cheap little tramp; he had actually called her one. Had she been the unscrupulous female he believed her to be, she would have run sobbing to Nicky with her tales of his ruthless, amoral father and Nicky would have angrily turned on Mark.

A clever woman could have taken Nicky for a ride without any trouble at all. Admitting that, she had to admit that Mark's attitude to her had been explicable. He must have personal experience of being pursued by greedy females and all the evidence had no doubt suggested that she was one of the breed who took naïve boys for every penny they could get out of them.

Coming out of the café they ran into a band of boys playing football in the car-park. Nicky kicked their ball, his black hair flying in the wind, then grinning triumphantly as it flew across the park, snatched

Rachel's hand and ran to their car with her, laughing at her.

As they reached the car she saw Mark lounging in
his seat, his eyes watching them in his driving mirror.
There was a narrowed fixity in his stare. She pulled her
hand from Nicky's, blushing, and Mark leaned over
to open the door for her.

'It's more comfortable in the back, Rachel,' Nicky
said with a plaintive little smile.

Mark started the engine, his eyes to the front. Rachel
turned to smile at Nicky, spreading her shoulders in
a shrug. The car was already in motion. Nicky sank
back, scowling. Rachel felt the brief, sideways flick of
Mark's dark lashes. He had no intention of allowing
her to sit in the back with his son.

It was then that she knew for certain that she had
been invited on this visit to their country house for a
purpose. Mark Hammond had tried other avenues to
discredit her in his son's eyes. This was another of his
plans. She was here for one purpose only—to make
sure that Nicky got the point that she was way above
his age bracket. Nicky was to be separated from her by
hook or by crook. Mark Hammond wanted her right
out of the picture.

CHAPTER FIVE

THEY drove up to Ambreys at sunset, the sky behind the creamy gothic outline of the roof a wash of crimson which gave a dramatic backcloth to the fretted stone and the darkening trees around it. The house was set in gardens and parkland which were all scrupulously maintained, their perfection a little too careful for Rachel's taste. The house itself was eighteenth-century, the style baroque; the local stone romantically over-decorated in a bizarre mixture of Moorish slits and geometric patterns with Norman spires.

'A gigantic folly,' she commented, and Mark's black head swung to survey her, a glint of amusement in his eyes.

'In more ways than one!'

She frowned, looking back at him. 'What does that mean?'

'I'm talking about my own folly in keeping it—a white elephant of a house I almost never visit. I keep telling myself I'll sell it.'

Nicky leaned forward in protest. 'No, Mark, you wouldn't.'

His father shrugged casually. 'Wouldn't I?'

Rachel looked towards the house. 'I see your point. But who would want to buy it? It's so big.'

Reading her tone he asked drily, 'And ugly?'

Nicky stirred incredulously and Rachel gave him a little smile. 'Oh, never ugly,' she told them both in a firm voice. 'Strange, unique even—never ugly. It has too much character. A living personality.'

The car slid round to come to rest outside the twin front steps leading to the pillared portico. Glancing up, Mark gave a slow smile. 'Talking of living personality . . . Olly is eager to meet you.'

Rachel followed the glance and saw a small figure leaning on the stone balustrade. The great bulk of the house left this side of it in shadow now that the sun had sunk. By the uncertain gleam of carriage lanterns hanging on each side of the polished double door, Rachel could only see a dark outline. Small as a child, it stayed immobile, staring down, the light gleaming dimly on silvery hair.

Mark came round and opened the door and reluctantly Rachel got out. A moment later the figure above was skimming down the stairs so fast it barely seemed to touch them.

With a nervous look, Rachel waited. Nicky had clambered out and was on one side of her, Mark standing on the other, his hand just resting on her shoulder as though supporting her for an ordeal.

The flying figure stopped dead, staring at the three of them. There was a silence.

'Rachel.' The name was spoken very clearly, softly, and the hair on the back of her neck seemed to stir as if at a premonition. Unconsciously she had tensed as if in fear of attack, her rounded body stiff.

'Olly!' Mark spoke sharply for some reason and the little figure moved closer then, holding out both hands.

Rachel found her own hands taken, squeezed. She stared. Old woman or child? In the shadowy light she

saw fine thick hair like beaten silver, disarranged with
charming effect, tendrils straying here and there across
thin, frail temples. The face was soft-skinned, lined like
a faintly wrinkled kid glove, delicately pink and white,
powdery with age.

Tiny, fragile and wiry at the same time, the small
body was dressed in a dark blue woollen dress with a
lacy collar and cuffs. She looked quickly at the eyes.
She had always found that eyes are rarely liars. They
betray emotion if not thought. These eyes were so
like Mark's that her breath caught in her throat. Dark
blue, enormous, smiling, they were filled with warmth.

'Are we going to stand here all night or shall we go
in?' Mark sounded irritable.

The peculiar enclosing silence ended so abruptly
that Rachel was stunned as Olly burst into quick, light
eager speech. 'Oh, Robbins will come and put away the
car. Robbins, are you there?' A tall thin man moved
from behind her. 'The car, Robbins, and bring in the
cases, will you? Come along, all of you. You must be
tired. We expected you hours ago. I thought you were
leaving early. Where on earth did you get to? Did
you have a good journey, Rachel? Nicky, you can't
walk alongside like that, dear boy—there isn't room.
Don't sulk now. Did you have lunch somewhere? Are
you hungry? I suppose you stopped somewhere, or
did the car break down? It seems to be perfectly all
right now. Did you have trouble with traffic?'

Rachel was breathless just listening to her. The
stream of questions and comment poured out without
the hint of a pause, and while she talked fast the old
woman was moving up the steep steps without any
sign of difficulty or weariness.

Mark broke in on one of the questions, his voice calm and faintly indulgent. 'We had lunch on the way— that's why we're late. Nicky saw some canoes on the lake at the restaurant, insisted on going out in one and got stuck on an island for three-quarters of an hour.'

The smooth tone hid the anger he had betrayed when they finally got back to the restaurant. Nicky had insisted on exploring an island in the middle of the lake, drawing the canoe up the muddy bank, but it had somehow drifted away while they were wandering among the thin trees. They had had to wait until the boatman came along and got them, having seen their canoe drifting empty.

Mark's eyes had been icy as they joined him. Nicky had looked quite beaten, although his father had said little.

Rachel suspected that Nicky had precipitated that incident because of a desire to assert himself—she had given way to his pleading over the canoe because his eyes had been so miserable. They had left Mark in the restaurant while they walked down to the lake. He had had no idea of Nicky's intention and when they at last rejoined him he had been fiercely out of temper.

The temper was aimed at herself, she knew very well. Mark thought she was still manoeuvring to hold Nicky. The silent battle between them was unnecessary, but if she told him that he would not believe her. Mark had begun by angrily despising her as a cheap gold-digger. Now, she suspected, he feared her. Nicky's unaltering adoration had worried him. Mark had been so sure he could kick her out of Nicky's life. He had tried bribery. He had tried to seduce her. He had threatened, scorned, tried to lower her in Nicky's eyes. It had all been unavailing. Now he was bitterly determined to fight the danger he thought she represented to his son with any weapon in his power.

In a way, his deepening fear of her was flattering. Mark no longer dismissed her with a shrug of those broad shoulders. His blue eyes held wary bitterness when he looked at her.

She had told him it would not even cross her mind to marry Nicky, but Mark did not believe her. He had seen her tenderness to the boy and had misread it.

The trouble was, Rachel decided, that Mark's altered attitude had had an unfortunate effect on Nicky. He sensed competition from his father, the rival his subconscious most feared, and his adoration of her had been given a new spur.

Mark would have been wiser to ignore her. He could have taken Nicky off to the States and time would have done the rest. Instead, he was throwing them together in the hope of disillusioning Nicky.

Rachel followed the others into the great baronial hall, torn between amazement and amusement as she looked around it. Stags' heads and faded banners hung from the walls. The dark beams crossed the vaulted ceiling in serried ranks. The antique lamps hid modern electricity. It was all so unreal that her eyes held laughter as they met Olly's blue gaze.

Olly smiled back at her. 'My dear, Nicky has told me so much about you!'

Rachel could guess at the reluctance with which Nicky had spoken, but she smiled back. 'I'm sure he's told me far more about you, Mrs Hammond.'

'Everyone calls me Olly. I hope you will too, because I want to call you Rachel. Such a lovely name. It suits you, too.'

'Thank you,' Rachel said softly.

Olly regarded her with a thoughtful face, then turned and a new burst of quick, light words. came from her as she addressed her son. Rachel was not listening. She had moved to the enormous fireplace and was staring at the artificial log fire. The hall was centrally heated; she sensed the pervading warmth around her. A great deal of money must have been spent on this place, and for what? Most of the year it was empty. It irritated her to think of that.

Nicky joined her and whispered, 'I'm sorry about the canoe, Rachel.'

She turned her head to smile at him. 'Forget it.'

'Mark's furious. I was an idiot.'

'So you were,' she agreed, but with a smiling look.

Nicky laughed reluctantly and touched her cheek with one hand. 'You have a very forgiving nature.'

She moved away and caught Mark's cold stare on them. Olly said briskly, 'Rachel, you'll want to see your room. Preskitt will take you up. Where is she? Stupid woman, she's vanished again. She was here a minute ago. Oh, those dogs! Who let them out? I shut them in the sitting-room.'

They were gambolling like lambs, their short legs twinkling, their pointy ears like foxes, yapping around Olly in open eagerness. Olly smiled at her. 'My corgis ... I've three now. I got two because I think they should always be kept in pairs. Gregarious animals, my dear. They need company. It's unkind to keep one dog unless you can spare a lot of time to it. But I let Bess have puppies—so much kinder before you have a bitch neutered. It spoils their nature if you don't let them have puppies once. Joey here was the result ... I gave the others away.'

'You should have given Joey away,' Mark said drily. 'He's worse than his parents put together. His teeth-marks are everywhere.'

Olly bent and picked up the sandy little dog, scooped him under one arm where he wriggled in an attempt to lick her face.

'I didn't mean to keep him.' She sounded apologetic. 'But he was so sweet I couldn't resist him.'

Mark grimaced. 'Sweet? That object?'

Olly bristled. 'Don't you think so, Rachel?'

Rachel laughed. 'I must admit I do.'

Mark's narrowed eyes were sardonic. 'I'll take Rachel up to her room.'

Nicky stirred and Olly pushed the corgi into his arms. 'Darling, put the dogs out of sight for me before your father gets into a temper, will you?'

Rachel followed Mark up the broad staircase. They mounted two flights and emerged on to a wide land-ing. He led her towards a room overlooking the gar-den. It was beautifully furnished, light and comfort-able. Mark leaned on the closed door and watched her move around. She was uneasy at his continuing presence.

At last she had to turn and face him, her head up in defiance. Their eyes fenced silently.

'What are you up to, Rachel?' Mark asked very quietly.

She widened her eyes. 'I don't understand you.'

'You understand me perfectly. It's I who doesn't understand you. With one hand you push Nicky away, with the other you beckon. What's your real plan for him?'

'I don't have any plans.'

His hard mouth tightened. 'Come off it!'

She leaned against the wooden bedhead, her face cool. 'You must make up your own mind about the plans you seem to imagine I have. I've told you several times. I'm sick of repeating myself.'

The blue eyes were intent under the black brows. 'Are you in love with him?'

Wearily she said, 'I've told you that that's absurd.'

'You've told me. Have you told him?' He took a few steps towards her. 'If you really care what happens to Nicky you'll lay it on the line for him.'

'I have!'

'He doesn't believe you! And neither, frankly, do I. You say one thing, you act another. Do you think I've missed the way you let him touch you?'

Her face flushed deeply. 'You make that sound terrible, but the sickness is in you, not me. I've never let Nicky make love to me, if that's what you mean.'

He was nearer and her pulses were beating that heavy drum-roll again. She looked at him, barely seeing him through the haze of excitement which was misting her vision.

'A woman can always say no with conviction. You aren't.'

'You refuse to understand. The conviction is there. I just can't hurt him that badly.'

'Why not?' Mark took further steps and they were face to face, his eyes inches away, his features taut, a dark hostility in his face.

Rachel shifted, her face uncertain. 'I hate hurting people.'

His hands shot out and imprisoned her face, tightening until they were crushing her bones like matchwood. 'I could like hurting you, Rachel. It's something I increasingly want to do.'

She breathed as though she were drowning. 'Let me go, Mark.'

'Put conviction into it, Rachel,' he said mockingly, then he bent his head and took her mouth.

She stood very still, her hand on his lean chest, resting there, not pushing him away. She was fighting a desire to put her arms around his neck, to cling. His lips moved powerfully against her own, parting them. She began to shake, terrified of her own emotions. His long-fingered hands stroked over her back, arching her towards him, exerting pressure she could not fight. As their bodies touched she felt a deep pulsing start inside her, a hot sweetness which pierced like a lance.

'No,' she moaned against his invading mouth, but she was talking to herself, denying aloud the sensations which were taking over her own body.

Mark drew back and looked at her, arrogance and passion in his dark face. 'Put it on the line for me too, Rachel. Is it a no without question, or haven't I made the right offer yet?'

Her green eyes were molten with anger. 'Buy yourself another woman, Mr Hammond. This one isn't for sale!'

'Did I mention money?' His hand was under her tumbled hair, stroking her nape. 'What do you want, Rachel? There has to be something. Name it.' His eyes were on her mouth. 'Just name it.'

Suddenly she could hear the deep fast beating of his heart, a thud like the crash of a hammer. The fingers caressing her were not quite steady. She looked into his eyes and her own heart turned over.

'I want you,' Mark whispered. He buried his face in her neck, kissing the warm skin hungrily. 'Rachel.'

The sharp, insistent temptation had her by the throat at that moment. Mark's voice, face, touch made his desire for her plain and weakness invaded her limbs. She felt she was falling. She slid her hands up his chest and clung to his shoulders, her head drooping back so that his exploring mouth could range freely over her throat. What did it matter? she asked herself weakly. Betrayed by her own need, she made no attempt to escape, trembling as his encroaching mouth came back to find her lips.

My God, she thought suddenly, what am I doing? What self-respect would she have left once she had allowed Mark to take her? Not a syllable of love had passed his lips. The burning hunger in his kisses was fuelled by physical desire, not emotion. With stark clarity her brain flashed the message angrily to her body and the sweet drowning sensuality was shut off as though by a tap. She stiffened and fought her way out of his arms. He grabbed at her, but she whisked away, her face white now.

Mark thrust his hands into his pockets, eyes cold and sharp.

'A new variation? You play an odd game.'

'I decided I didn't want anything you could offer.' She spoke the words icily, dropping them at his feet.

His face tautened. 'Have you explored all the possibilities? I'm not only a very rich man, I'm a powerful one. I can reach down any toy from the Christmas tree, Rachel. Think about it.' He looked her up and down. 'That husky little voice of yours is not likely to make you a star; sexy you may be, but you need more than that to go to the top. I could buy you publicity that would make you famous.'

She shook her head. 'Sorry. Not interested.'

His eyes were fiery. 'Damn you, what do you want?'

'I told you, nothing you can give me.'

'It's Nicky.' He said it flatly, watching her.

She was bitterly angry. 'If that's what you care to believe.'

'A seventeen-year-old?' His lips drew back in a snarl. 'Are you some sort of freak?'

'Definitely.' Rachel badly wanted him to get out of this room. She would have said anything just then to make him go. Her body was aching and she was afraid she would humiliate herself by weeping in front of him.

'Then you lied before? I suspected it, but I couldn't be sure.' He was watching her strangely, a mixture of anger and compassion now in his dark face. 'You can't marry him, for God's sake.'

'I have no intention of marrying him.' That much she could say in a clear, confident tone. That much was the truth.

He was silent. After a moment he asked deeply, 'Is he your lover?'

'Of course not!' Rachel glared at him, infuriated by the question. 'Nicky is a charming boy but that's all he is ... a boy.'

He sounded impatient, angry. 'Then what in heaven's name are you getting out of it?'

'You think like a machine, Mr Hammond, a computer, not a man, and computers are notoriously unreliable. They depend on a programmer to feed them the right information and then they react logically, but logic is often mistaken because it takes no account of factors it isn't programmed to consider.'

His mouth compressed tightly, a dark glow about his features. 'Such as?'

She spread her hands in a shrug. 'You see everything in terms of profit and loss. There always has to be a motive, you told me. Well, I don't talk that sort of language, and I'm not going to discuss the subject with you.'

Mark had thrust his hands into his pockets, but now one hand came up and caught her chin between strong fingers. He tilted it gently and looked into her eyes.

'If you really aren't after Nicky, let me make love to you.'

Her breath caught harshly. She froze, staring at him.

'I'm told I'm a good lover,' he went on coolly. 'You wouldn't regret it. If you're honest you'll admit you wouldn't find it any hardship.' He put his other hand against her face, softly following the outline of her cheekbones.

She watched his face with a rapidly beating heart and knew that she was half-way to being in love with him. It would not take much more to push her over the edge into a bitter, intense passion.

'I'm sure you make love very well, Mr Hammond,' she drawled with a sweet smile. 'I'll admit I was quite impressed by your technique. But I'm afraid I just don't fancy you.'

His face toughened, his eyes flashed angrily. Dark

red came up under the skin stretched tautly across his cheekbones.

'Why, you little ...' He bit off the words, his teeth clamping together in open fury, then he dragged her towards him with an intention which needed no under-lining.

She put both hands against his broad shoulders and held him at a distance with difficulty. 'No, thank you. Once was enough!'

For a few seconds he looked angry enough to frighten anyone. 'You're trying my temper, Rachel,' he said through his teeth. 'Push me far enough and I'll strangle you with my bare hands.'

'Now that I can believe!' she said sweetly. 'Violence is probably your forte even if lovemaking isn't.'

The blue eyes burned with temper. He stared at her, visibly fighting for control, his fingers biting into her flesh like steel claws.

'I can't buy you, seduce you, threaten you,' he said thickly. 'You're forcing me to consider less pleasant methods, Miss Austen.'

She gave him a dry little smile, her lashes flicking over him in derision. 'You're pathetic, Mr Hammond. You're so accustomed to your own way that you rage like a child when it's refused you.'

The contempt bit home; Mark's face flushed dark red. For a second she thought he was coming back, rage in his eyes. Then he went out and slammed the door.

When she came back downstairs later she found them all in the long salon. Olly's quick high speech caught her ears before she entered the room. A servant directed her, giving her a curious look.

The room was panelled in white wood inset with gold, the furnishings impersonally magnificent. Ambreys was not a home, it was a showplace, a demonstration of the power of money.

As she walked into the room Mark was speaking in a cold, hard voice. 'He lied about it, but the evidence is overwhelming. The man's guilty. I have to make an example of him.'

'His poor wife and children,' Olly said mournfully. 'I met her in New York two years ago, a nice creature. It seems a shame that they should suffer for his weakness.'

'He embezzled fifty thousand dollars,' said Mark. 'He has to pay.'

Olly turned her head as Rachel walked in to greet them, smiling at her warmly. 'Ah, there you are, my dear. Nicky, get Rachel a drink. What will you have, Rachel? What a pretty dress, such a charming colour, and you look enchanting in it, doesn't she, Mark?' She turned her face towards her son with a smile.

His dark blue eyes roved insolently down Rachel's body in the clinging green silk. 'Enchanting.' The word was spoken with deliberate, offensive meaning.

His mother's brows drew together. Rachel looked back at Mark, her face cool and bland.

'Thank you.' Nicky, frowning, handed her a Martini, his eyes angry.

He turned and glared at his father. Mark leaned back in his chair and met the boy's stare without expression.

It was the opening shot in a campaign which lasted all evening. Mark was intent on insulting her now. Every word, every look, made his hatred and distaste

for her obvious. He brought his son to the point of open anger and quite plainly distressed his mother.

His behaviour surprised Rachel. He had shown more finesse in earlier encounters. He was behaving now like a bull in a china shop, the harsh brutal treatment alienating Nicky, throwing away all the work he had put in on the boy in earlier time.

She was glad when the evening ended and she could escape to her own room. Alone, she sat on her bed and contemplated Mark's behaviour with bewilderment. She had thought him cleverer than that.

When the door opened she looked up in alarm, but it was Olly, in a white dressing-gown, her hair brushed for the night into a plait. She looked tentatively at Rachel. 'May I come in, my dear?'

'Please do.' Rachel stood up, wondering why the other woman had come, expecting at once to hear yet another plea to leave Nicky alone.

Olly sat down on the bed and patted it. 'Do sit down, Rachel.'

Rachel obeyed slowly and they eyed each other.

'Now,' Olly said softly, 'what's wrong with Mark?'

Rachel's mouth took on crooked humour. 'You tell me.'

Olly laughed, mischief in her blue eyes. 'I'm only his mother. I rarely get the truth from him.'

Rachel laughed. 'From what Nicky has told me about you, I suspect he respects you and loves you very much.'

'Nicky does?'

'Well, both,' Rachel expanded.

The soft, wrinkled face looked tranquil under the rope of white hair. 'What happened between you and

Mark tonight? He changed between when you arrived and when you came down to dinner.'

Passing a nervous tongue tip over her lips, Rachel said huskily, 'We quarrelled.'

'I'm going to be frank with you,' said Olly, watching her. She put out a hand and patted Rachel's hands. 'I think I can be frank. You have eyes I trust—they're clear and direct. If I offend you in anything I say, I hope you'll tell me so.' She looked sharply at Rachel. 'When I first heard of your existence I was upset, and I sent for Mark at once. He came, and we both agreed that you must be eliminated.'

Rachel's brows rose at the word and Olly laughed. 'Oh, I didn't exactly mean that. We thought you were a mercenary little baggage who'd somehow trapped Nicky. Mark went to see you to buy you off.' Olly gave her a sharp little grin, her eyes wicked. 'I'm afraid I had to do as much for Mark when he was a boy.'

Rachel's eyes widened. 'You did?'

'You can't imagine it?' Olly laughed. 'Oh, yes, Mark made a fool of himself once or twice. He's attractive to women, and several times he got entangled with the wrong sort.'

'I thought he married very young?'

Olly's eyes narrowed as she looked at her. 'You think marriage should end such problems? Well, of course you're right, but Mark's marriage was one of convenience. He married money. He never loved his wife and she knew it. They disliked each other—that's why they rarely saw each other after Nicky was born. His wife resented her marriage. She disliked Mark. She brought Nicky up to hate his father.'

'Nicky hinted as much,' Rachel admitted.

Olly sighed. 'Mark is a strange man. He was a difficult boy, too precocious by far. When he was eighteen he was already in control of a big business. He tasted power too soon and it's corrupted his own intelligence, and the women he has around him have continued the corruption. He's hard, ruthless and arrogant.' Her lined face held sadness. 'I love him very much, but I often wish I didn't. I wish it didn't worry me so much to see what happened to him. That was why I wanted Nicky. I failed with Mark; I didn't want to fail with his son.'

'You didn't,' Rachel said quickly, reassuringly. 'Nicky is a fine boy. He'll make a wonderful man one day.'

Olly put both hands around hers. 'If he goes to the States with Mark, though, what effect will that have on him? He's come under his father's influence at a difficult time. He's just passing into the adult world. He admires Mark. He's absorbing life from him every day —seeing it through his father's eyes, and what Mark sees isn't pretty; I realised that within a short time. It hadn't occurred to me that Mark would take the boy away from me when I sent for him. Mark has always stayed at a distance from Nicky. Now he's taking the boy around with him all day and Nicky is learning the wrong things.'

Rachel gave a troubled sigh. Olly was putting her own views into words. 'I'm afraid you're right.'

Olly sighed in satisfaction. 'Then you do agree?'

'I wish I didn't.'

Olly leant forward and kissed her cheek. 'I was right to come to you. I'm so glad. My dear, the solution is in your hands.'

Rachel stared, bewildered. 'Mine?'

Olly nodded soberly. 'Mark is only taking Nicky to America because he wants to get him away from you. If you were out of the picture, Mark would let me keep Nicky safely in London.'

Rachel understood then. She looked at Olly drily. 'I see. You want me to vanish?'

'Completely,' Olly said very gently. 'Nicky will look for you. He mustn't find you.'

Rachel did not know what to say. 'I have a job, a career, friends ...'

'I promise that none of those things will suffer. I can see to it that you get a job.' Olly pursed her pale lips. 'Have you ever considered the Bahamas? I have a friend with a club over there who would give you a singing engagement. Well paid, I assure you. You won't lose by doing this.'

Rachel took a moment to think. With a sigh, she said, 'I'll go.'

Olly closed her eyes, their lined blue lids trembling. 'Thank you, Rachel. Now, you mustn't say a word to any of them. Total secrecy. This is between you and me.'

Rachel nodded. 'I promise.'

Olly smiled at her. 'You're a very nice girl. I'm not surprised that both Mark and Nicky should care for you.'

Rachel's face froze. Her eyes held pain. 'Mark?' The word held fierce question. 'Why should you think he cares for me?'

Olly met her eyes directly, her face grave. 'Doesn't he?'

'He hates me.'

Olly gave a dry little smile. 'When he first met you,

I knew you attracted him. I know him too well to be deceived. You maddened him, you put him into a blazing temper. But when he talked about you, I could tell he found you atractive. Tonight, seeing you together, it was very obvious. I don't know what Mark has done to you, but I know him too well to miss the signs. He can't take his eyes off you. He was extremely rude all evening—anyone could be forgiven for thinking he loathed you, but every time he speaks to you or looks at you he gives himself away.'

Rachel was hotly flushed, her eyes disturbed. With a flash of temper she said, 'Do you really want to know what your son wants?' She broke off, aghast. How could she say such a thing to his mother?

Olly laughed drily. 'He wants to make you his mistress?'

Rachel's face jerked into surprised embarrassment.

'I'm not a child,' said Olly. 'I guessed that. When Mark wants something he can't have, he gets violent. He isn't used to self-denial, but it might be good for him.' Her eyes were amused. 'It might do him a great favour. It's time he discovered he can't have everything he wants.' She glanced slyly at Rachel. 'I am right in thinking you've turned him down?'

'Flat!' said Rachel with a snap, her teeth coming together sharply.

Olly looked satisfied. 'Tell me, did Nicky ever ask you to marry him?'

Rachel smiled. 'Frequently.'

'He got the same reply as his father?'

Rachel looked at her with impatience. 'Of course. Mrs Hammond, I'm fond of Nicky, very fond, but he's still half a child.'

Olly nodded. 'And Mark?'

Rachel looked away. 'He's detestable.'

'Was it difficult?' Olly sounded gentle yet amused.

Rachel looked back at her questioning, 'What?'

'Saying no when you wanted to say yes?' The old face held a tender teasing. 'You did want to say yes, I suspect?'

Rachel put her hands over her face, shuddering. 'Desperately.'

Olly put both arms around her, kissing her forehead. 'My dear, I'm afraid you're as obvious as Mark. I only had to see you together for two minutes to know.' She stood up and yawned. 'Now, enjoy your visit while you're here, Rachel. I shall attend to the details of your new job. When you leave here you should be able to fly straight to the Bahamas.'

Rachel gave a weary smile. 'Such is the power of money! Every little problem ironed out in a second.'

Olly looked back at her, her blue eyes gentle. 'I wish I could do more for you, but I think you'd refuse, wouldn't you?' Rachel's smile was answer enough.

CHAPTER SIX

WHEN she came down to breakfast next morning she found Mark at the table, reading his *Times*, the black head hidden behind the opened pages. An array of breakfast dishes stood on the sideboard. Rachel helped herself to tomatoes and bacon, sat down and spread a slice of toast with butter. Mark spoke without lowering his newspaper.

'I'm sorry.'

She looked up, her knife suspended. For a moment she thought she had misheard. 'Did you say something?'

He dropped the paper slightly and his blue eyes guardedly met her stare. 'You heard what I said.'

There was a slight trace of red along his cheekbones and his mouth was level.

'As an apology, that's hardly worth noticing.' She went on spreading the butter, her head bent. Turning to her breakfast, she began to eat slowly. The bacon was slightly salty, a pleasant flavour, cooked crisply just as she liked it.

'Do you want me to go down on my knees?' He sounded sulky, as though hating what he had just said, resenting the necessity to apologise. She wondered if Olly had persuaded him to do it.

Mischief lit her green eyes, but she kept them fixed on her plate. 'Yes, please,' she said.

There was a moment's astounded silence, then he

laughed. She lifted her eyes to his face and he grinned at her, the hard lines of eyes, nose, mouth relaxed and softened. 'You little bitch!' He sounded admiring, amused. Getting up, he threw down his paper and walked round towards her. She watched him in suspended animation.

He went down on his knees, his mouth crooked, putting both hands together as though he prayed. 'Mea culpa,' he intoned piously.

Green eyes melting with amusement, Rachel shook her head. 'I ought to smack your face.'

He reached out, took one of her hands and laid it against his own cheek, rubbing his skin over the back of it. 'What can I say? I've never met anyone like you in my life. I don't know how to deal with you, Rachel. I'm entirely at a loss with you.' He sounded serious, his eyes on her face. 'If you're for real, you're worth your weight in rubies.'

'A much over-estimated stone,' she retorted.

He laughed. 'I can't buy you, bribe you, seduce you . . . what am I going to do with you?'

'Kill me, apparently,' she reminded him.

He groaned. 'Oh, hell, I was just chucking my weight around. You know I didn't mean that.'

She arched an eyebrow. 'No? You could have fooled me.'

'You have. Consistently.' Mark frowned, the black brows heavy above the blue eyes. 'You come from a world I never knew existed. That cousin of yours is from one box, you're from another. I've come to a conclusion about you. Do you want to know what it is?'

'I'll have to hear it sooner or later, so why not now?' Rachel watched his face absorbedly, her heart thudding. When he was in this mood he was devastating. His smile made her pulses go crazy.

'You're entirely free of self-interest, aren't you?' The blue eyes were grave. 'That was something I couldn't believe. I thought that all I had to do was probe deep enough and I'd come up with your secret motive. I sat up all night trying to work you out.' He rubbed a hand over his eyes. 'I caught a couple of hours' sleep once I'd knocked myself out with half a decanter of whisky, then when I woke up the answer flashed into my brain.' He stared at her, all the hard lines of his face intent. 'You don't want anything.'

She laughed almost wildly. 'Congratulations! Logic finally worked it out. Your programmer is to be congratulated.'

Mark's colour darkened. 'I deserved that.' He stood up, looking down at her. 'How the hell was I to guess? All my life people have queued up to squeeze something out of me—money, position, status, possessions. I can't be blamed if I wasn't expecting to meet the one in a million who didn't want anything.'

'Can I eat my breakfast now?' Rachel turned back to her food, her face calm. Mark stood for a moment, watching her, then he walked round the table and sat down. He picked up *The Times* and shook it out with a rustle. She sensed that her reaction to his apology had ruffled him. Mark had felt very generous in conceding it, and he was irritated that she had not been more pleased.

Nicky walked into the silence, whistling cheerfully. 'Good morning!'

Rachel smiled at him. 'Good morning, Nicky. You look as if you slept well.'

'Like a top.' He moved past her, brushing the top of her head with a light kiss, and selected some breakfast. Mark looked at her over the top of his paper, his eyes very dark. She looked down, finishing her breakfast.

'This morning I'm going to show you all over the estate.' Nicky sat down and she poured him some coffee. 'I want you to see every inch of it.'

'I'd love that.' She sipped her own coffee. Mark put down his paper and nodded to Nicky.

There was cold tension in Nicky's young face. 'Good morning, Father.' He used the name deliberately and she saw he was still angry about the way Mark had behaved to her all the previous evening. He turned his head to look at Rachel. 'First of all, I'll show you the White Gallery. It's full of ivory, hence the name. The ivory was brought here from India by someone in the nineteenth century, though I'm afraid some of it's in a poor state—it was badly stored and has decayed. There's nothing that can be done to restore it.'

Mark got up and walked out of the room. Nicky looked after him with a bitter expression. 'I'm sorry if my father upset you, Rachel.' He looked at her unhappily. 'He's behaving very strangely.'

'He's already apologised,' she said soothingly. 'Please, forget it, Nicky. Don't quarrel with him over me.'

Nicky looked uncertain. 'He apologised?'

She laughed. 'Don't sound so amazed! Yes, he really did! Quite fulsomely.'

Nicky sighed. 'Well, that's something. He just doesn't know you, Rachel.'

As the morning wore on, Rachel's feet and calves ached. Nicky seemed tireless, walking from room to room in the enormous house and then dragging her after him around the extensive gardens. Ambreys was a revelation to her of how money could be used to fertilise beauty. The care which had been taken to preserve so unlikely a building surprised her. Gothic charm had never bitten her before, but she began to feel a peculiar vibrating pleasure in the bizarre house.

The gardens were separated by walls, hedges, terraces, one succeeding another. One was called the Blue Garden, the flowers all shades of blue from delphinium to forget-me-not. The effect was restful and calming. Beyond that was the herbaceous garden, the mixed array of different leaves a bouquet of greens and silvers. One garden contained palm trees which left a Mediterranean impression on the eye, their leaves serrated against the blue of the sky, a brilliant tropical garden beneath them, all oranges and reds.

Rachel sank on to a stone seat at last, rubbing her calves. 'Nicky, I'm dead beat!' She gave him a weary smile. 'I've got to rest for a while.'

He sat down beside her, stretching his long thin body. 'But you do like Ambreys?'

'Who could fail to like it?'

'Mark could,' he said, grimacing. 'You heard him. He'd like to sell it.'

'It's his house!'

Nicky looked sulky. 'One day it would be mine.'

Rachel frowned. 'Your father's not forty yet, Nicky. You can expect him to live for another forty years, I've no doubt. He seems tough enough to live to be a hundred.' Her voice was wry. 'I shouldn't count any chickens, if I were you.'

'I love Ambreys,' Nicky said childishly. 'It's the nearest thing to a home I've got.'

'Poor Nicky!'

He caught the faintly teasing note and laughed reluctantly. They sat side by side in silence, enjoying the morning warmth. The sun was almost directly overhead. A faint wind moved among the flowers, wafting their strong perfume towards Rachel and Nicky. A thrush sat on a stone wall, singing his heart out, apparently as much rejoicing in the morning as they did.

'I could stay here all day,' she said, deeply relaxed.

Nicky moved restlessly. 'I want to show you the stables now, Rachel. You haven't seen my horse.'

She groaned. 'What it is to be seventeen!'

'You sound as if twenty-five was a terrific age,' he grunted, eyeing her disgustedly.

Her eyes danced. 'Believe me, it feels like it after you've dragged me on a ten-mile hike around Ambreys!'

He rested his elbow on the back of the seat, his face turned towards her, the black hair flopping over his forehead. 'You look fantastic in that outfit, Rachel.'

She looked down at her lime green dress, arching a quizzical eyebrow. 'Why, thank you, Nicky.'

He was silent. 'Olly and I had a chat last night. She doesn't want me to go to the States with Mark. I was quite surprised—she was really upset to think of me leaving her.' He looked very young and uncertain, his thin face tense. 'She's old, you know, Rachel, I mean really old, and she won't leave London, but she'll miss me if I go. I never thought of that. I didn't think she would mind. But she'll be lonely.'

Rachel watched him. 'It has to be your decision, Nicky. You'll be eighteen very soon. What do you want to do?'

'I don't know.' He sighed deeply. 'I want to go with

Mark, but I don't want to leave Olly. What shall I do, Rachel?'

'Follow your heart,' she said quietly. 'It's the only worthwhile guide. Olly has brought you up; it's understandable if she feels sad at the thought of you going away, especially as her son will be in the States too.'

Nick nodded, his mouth quivering. 'Mark's quite something, Rachel, but ...' He broke off and she waited patiently, watching him.

He looked at her. 'He isn't always easy to like. He's hard, very hard. Look at the way he's behaved to you. I didn't like that. He can't seem to see things the way I do.' He was trying to explain to himself as much as to her, his voice uncertain.

'He's much older,' Rachel pointed out. 'He lives and survives in a jungle. Maybe jungle laws are all he understands. It might be wise for you to find out about that jungle, Nicky. On the other hand, it might be wiser if you never found out. But you would have to be careful to keep out of the jungle later.'

Nicky smiled. 'I get the point. Maybe I'll stay in London with Olly for a while. Maybe later I'll visit Mark's jungle.'

Rachel felt an intolerable relief. 'When you're older and wiser,' she said huskily. 'You'll be able to survive in that jungle in a few years without coming out of it with an incurable disease.'

Nicky looked at her hard. 'Like Mark?'

She met his glance. 'I'm afraid so. Perhaps he went into the jungle too soon. It's marked him.'

Nicky nodded. 'Come on, I'll take you to the stables.'

She stood up, groaning. 'If I can totter there.'

He laughed, watching her put a hand to her aching back. 'Poor old lady!'

The half patronising tone struck her. She gave no sign of any reaction, but she wondered if it was the beginning of the end as far as Nicky's enthralled infatuation was concerned. Mark's influence on him had been sharp and profound. Even in so short a time Nicky had grown up rapidly. He was thinking for himself and thinking sanely. His decision to stay with Olly was based on affection and common sense. He had a deep loyalty which so far had only been tapped by Olly and herself, and more recently, perhaps by Mark a little, but Mark's influence seemed to have waned since Nicky observed how he behaved towards her. Nicky had gone back in spirit to his grandmother.

They wandered around the stables for half an hour, then went back to the house. At lunch Mark suggested a drive around the countryside near Ambreys. Nicky looked eager, but Olly said to him softly, 'Nicky, would you mind coming with me to see the Palfreys? I did promise Jane you would be there.'

Nicky looked disgusted. 'Jane Palfrey? Good lord, Olly, she's a real drag!'

'All the same, it would be polite for you to pay a little visit. The Palfreys have always been kind to you, remember. You owe it to them.'

Nicky gave Rachel and Mark an unhappy look, reluctance in every line of his face, but he went off with his grandmother in the end to pay his duty visit. Mark's mouth was wry.

'The Palfreys are old family friends,' he explained.

'And Jane is a suitable young girl for Nicky?' Rachel gave him a dry smile.

Mark watched her intently. 'Would you mind if I said yes?'

She shrugged. 'Not a bit. Nicky will marry when he's ready to marry, and I have too much respect for your mother to think she would try to force his hand.'

- 'Meaning what?'

She sighed. 'Meaning what it seems to mean—that Nicky will only be happy when he meets a girl of his own age and loves her. Anything else would be a recipe for disaster.'

'Coming for that drive?' Mark sounded abrupt as he rose. She followed, shrugging.

The countryside was rich and green; rolling downland giving way to woods, the haze of early summer hanging over the horizon, a faint pearly mist which hid heat. The echo of the cuckoo came across the fields. Mark parked the car on a hillside from which they could see the whole sweep of the land. They climbed a stile and walked through deep pasture to sit under an oak tree. The frilled green leaves interwove to give a cool shade. Sheep ambled amiably below them, one or two raising mild heads to stare incuriously at these interlopers.

Rachel picked a few long-stemmed buttercups, slitting the stems to weave them into a chain. Mark sat with his arms around his knees, his hands linked. The breeze blew through his black hair, lifting it to reveal the hard bones of his temples.

He watched her for a while without speaking. Then he said, 'You never did tell me about your parents.'

'They died. I was just old enough to remember them. At the time I used to wish I'd been younger. I would have got over it sooner. Now I'm glad I was old enough to know what I'd lost—it gave me something of my own to cling to when I was looking for myself.'

His eyes were piercing. 'Did you find yourself?'

She smiled, her eyes on the growing golden chain. 'Oh, yes.'

'When was this?'

She shrugged. 'I was eighteen.'

There was a silence. 'Nicky's age.'

Rachel looked up and her face was wry. 'Precisely.'

'Tell me about it.'

'It's a fairly ordinary little story. I imagine you can guess most of it.'

'An older man?'

'He would have to be, wouldn't he? He was married with kids, too. As I said, an ordinary story. Afterwards I felt lost, betrayed. It was then that remembering my parents helped. Derry was no use. His parents never even knew and I couldn't have told them. I had to find my own way out of it.'

Mark stared down into the valley, the sun glinting on the windows and roofs of a village far below.

'Why didn't you tell me this before?'

She had finished her chain and it hung swinging from her fingers, the metallic gleam of the flowers vivid.

'You wouldn't have listened and believed me then.'

He turned his black head and his face was heavy. 'My God, you make me feel a fool! I'm sorry, Rachel—I've been blind. I thought I knew it all, but even my own son was quicker to see the truth about you than I was.'

She smiled at him calmly. 'Nicky has been infatuated with me. He didn't really see me at all.'

Mark's eyes searched her face. 'You use the past tense.'

'I think so. Even the fiercest emotion fades in the

light. Nicky is already growing out of his crush on me.
You really had no need to sweat over it.'

Mark turned and stared down the valley again. 'You
could have told me all this that first time when I came
to your dressing-room.'

'I began to, but you made it clear you wouldn't
listen.' Her face contorted in a grimace. 'No, that's not
quite true. You made me angry and I behaved as
stupidly as you were doing.'

She got up and Mark got to his feet, too, looking
down at her with a strange expression. The strong fleshless face was totally serious. She looked down at the
buttercup chain, then on an impulse flung it round his
head.

'There you are, a crown for you! Real gold, too.
Priceless.'

He didn't laugh back at her. Slowly he eased the
chain around his neck, the golden flowers glittering in
the sunlight.

Rachel felt a peculiar stillness between them. She
flushed, quite inexplicably, turned and began to walk
back to the car.

Mark closed the door after her, walked round and
climbed in beside her. He sat with his hands on the
wheel, looking at his own fingers as though seeing them
for the first time.

'Have you been in love since that first time?' The
question took her off guard.

Huskily, Rachel said, 'No.' It was an effort to speak
the curt monosyllable. He was probing too close to
something painful.

The long fingers rapped on the wheel as though he
were thinking deeply. A car zoomed past and dust
flew up in white spirals behind it. Some cross rooks

clattered upward, raucously shrieking at it, then settled again on an elm nearby.

Mark started the engine and slid away down the road. Around his brown throat the buttercups swung vividly, already growing limp. Rachel looked at them against his skin and felt her mouth grow dry.

Ambreys came into view like an impossible dream in its woodland setting, the trees curving around it like cupped hands holding a chalice. The strange architecture looked absurdly solid in this very English scene.

'I've never been in love in my life,' Mark suddenly told her in a clipped voice.

Rachel's mouth quivered, but she held it steady. 'What an empty life, Mr Hammond.' She made the reply coolly dry and his black head jerked round to observe her.

His eyes held a brilliant glitter. 'I don't know if I even believe in the love you talk about.'

She shrugged. 'You have to be capable of it to believe in it.'

'I've always thought love was for blind men or fools.'

'They do both have something in common,' she agreed almost in amusement. 'They both see in a different dimension from yours.'

'And yours?' He was staring at her fixedly.

She smiled at him. 'And mine.'

'Yet you've never been in love since that first time?'

'One day I shall,' she said. 'I'm sure of that. If I have to wait a lifetime or even beyond.'

They pulled up outside Ambreys and she climbed out of the car.

Mark caught her arm above the elbow tightly, detaining her as she was walking into the house. 'Is that why you wouldn't let me become your lover?'

She looked down at his hand. 'Yes. Please let me go—you're hurting!'

'Don't lie,' he said, relaxing his fingers but still holding her. 'Did you want me, Rachel?'

She looked up, her heart sick. 'Yes,' she said, meeting his blue eyes, 'I wanted you. Now can we forget it?'

He was frowning as though an equation was too difficult for him, his eyes puzzled. She pulled at her arm and he let her go, following her slowly into the house.

Olly and Nicky came back from their visit to the Palfreys in hysterics. Nicky burst out with the story as soon as they appeared. Jane Palfrey, it seemed, had grown up with a vengeance. 'She was absolutely insatiable! Wasn't she, Olly? I was quite terrified. Talk about a man-eater! She sat there eating me with her eyes all the time and she had eye make-up at least two inches thick plastered around them. Someone ought to tell her to wipe off most of that stuff.'

Olly was laughing, too, but more kindly. 'Her spots have gone, poor child. That's one blessing for her.'

'Those jeans! She couldn't move in them.'

'They were rather tight,' Olly agreed, eyes twinkling.

'You must take her in hand, Rachel,' said Nicky. 'You always look fantastic.'

'I'm not seventeen,' Rachel said gently. 'When I was you should have seen me! Covered with spots and absurdly over-made-up.'

Mark came into the room while they were laughing, his eyes on Rachel's face. He had changed into a dark suit and the buttercups had gone, flung into a waste-paper basket, no doubt.

'I've invited the Palfreys to dinner,' Olly told them.

'Lord help us all,' Nicky chimed in, and his grandmother shook her head at him.

'Now, you'll be very kind to Jane, Nicky.'

'If I have to,' he groaned, moving off to change for dinner.

Olly looked at Rachel. 'Did you enjoy your drive?'

'This is a very beautiful part of the world,' Rachel agreed. 'Is Jane Palfrey as bad as Nicky says, or is he exaggerating?'

Olly laughed. 'He's exaggerating.'

'I suspected so,' said Rachel. 'She sounds rather sweet and I thought Nicky thought so, too.'

Olly gave her an appreciative nod. 'Quite right. You're very quick, Rachel. Nicky was impressed but patronising.'

'Poor Jane!' Rachel laughed. Mark had just stood there, listening, saying nothing. His mother went out and he pushed his hands into his pockets.

'I'm going out to dinner this evening,' he said. 'Do I gather we have visitors?'

'Not tonight—on Thursday, apparently.'

He stared down at his dark shoes. 'I see. Well, make my excuses to Olly, would you? I must go.' He turned and went quickly and she stared at the door in resignation.

Olly seemed unsurprised to hear that Mark had gone out to dinner. They dined cheerfully together, Nicky very lively and extrovert, his eyes sparkling. Olly came to Rachel's room later and told her that she had already spoken to her friend in the Bahamas. 'The job is yours from next week. Your fare will be paid as part of the salary. There's a chalet in the hotel grounds. You'll be singing once a night except on Sunday.' She named a salary, watching Rachel's face. 'Is that satisfactory?'

'Very,' said Rachel. It was, in fact, higher than the one she received from the Harem.

'Nicky has told me he'll stay in London,' Olly went on. 'I'm sure Mark will accept that.'

Rachel smiled brightly. 'Once he knows I'm out of the way.'

Olly nodded. 'I think that's essential, my dear.'

'It will be fun, actually,' Rachel said. 'All that sunshine and good living. It will spoil me for London.'

'That's a very sensible attitude.' Olly stood up. 'When you come back I hope you'll get in touch with me. I'll write to you, if I may, letting you know how Nicky is ...'

'Thank you, I'd be glad if you would.'

When Olly had gone, Rachel got into bed and lay in the darkness wondering why she felt so close to tears. It had nothing to do with leaving London or even leaving Nicky. It was Mark and she knew it, but there was absolutely no future in allowing him to penetrate her heart. He was incapable of love; he had said as much.

For the next few days she saw little of Mark. She rode with Nicky every morning before the day advanced, enjoying the leisurely moments in the early sunshine. His palomino was a beautiful animal, cream and gold, superbly bred, filled with temperament and good manners. The mare she rode was of a lesser quality, but sweet-natured and easy to manage.

The evening the Palfreys came to dinner Nicky was in high spirits. Jane Palfrey turned out to be a dark girl with big brown eyes and a smooth olive skin. Nicky was right when he said she wore too much make-up, but it would be a temporary matter, and watching Nicky tease her, Rachel was amused by his condescending manner, and even more amused by a fact which escaped him—Jane Palfrey was perfectly aware of his patronising attitude and boiling with resentment over it.

After dinner Olly sent them off to view the White Gallery. Rachel politely slipped away, leaving the younger two together. At the far end of the gallery she suddenly heard a roar of surprised outrage. She looked back and saw Nicky with a waste-paper basket on his head, a litter of paper around his feet. Jane was stalking off with her head high.

Rachel stuffed a fist into her mouth and vanished. Meeting Olly on the stairs a moment later she whispered the little incident to her and they both laughed.

When Nicky reappeared downstairs he had a dark, smouldering look which reminded Rachel of his father. Mark was talking to Mr Palfrey, a bald man with smooth manners. Jane was seated beside her mother looking deadpan. Nicky came in and sat down beside Rachel with a thump. She looked sideways at him, her mouth held strictly in control.

Her eyes, however, betrayed her to him. Leaning over, he whispered, 'What's funny?' and his angry blue stare fixed her.

She tried to smile placatorily at him. 'Nothing.'

Nicky glared. She looked away, biting her lip, and met Mark's long, cool appraisal. It was the first time for several days that he had looked at her, and she felt herself flush.

Nicky sprang up and stalked out. Jane Palfrey was staring at her. She came over and sat beside Rachel with a curious expression. Rachel smiled at her.

'I'm afraid I saw what you did to Nicky,' she told Jane. 'I couldn't help laughing. He deserved it.'

Jane gave a soft laugh. 'Well, it knocked him off his perch at any rate. I was sick of the airs he was giving

himself just because he's ...' She broke off and eyed
Rachel with a red face.

'Because he's what?' Rachel asked suspiciously.

'Well, he's rather proud of having a nightclub singer
for a girl-friend,' Jane muttered uneasily.

'A what?' Rachel gasped, then laughed wryly. 'That
boy! He needs spanking.'

'You mean you aren't? I mean ...'

'I'm not his girl-friend,' Rachel said firmly. 'Friend,
yes. The rest is his over-vivid imagination.'

Jane relaxed. 'Oh, really?' She looked more cheerful.
'Then I'm even more glad I slammed that waste-paper
basket over his head.'

'So am I,' said Rachel, and they both laughed.

When the Palfreys had gone Rachel slipped up to
her room. She lay in bed thinking about the Bahamas.
It might turn out to be a lucky decision for her, and
anyway it would get her away from any reminders of
Mark Hammond.

Next morning when she got downstairs she found
Olly at the breakfast table alone. The blue eyes lifted
in a smile. 'Good morning, my dear. I'm afraid you're
going to be left to my company this morning. Nicky
has gone over to the Palfrey house to have a row with
Jane and Mark has gone to London on business.'

Rachel fastened on the first piece of news to cover
her shock at the second. 'Poor Jane, I hope you gave
her warning?'

Olly laughed. 'Certainly not! It will be much more
fun for Nicky if he takes her by surprise, and he's burning for revenge.'

'So is Jane,' said Rachel, and told her what Jane had
confided to her the previous night.

As she ate her breakfast she said, 'It occurs to me

that now would be a good time for me to do my vanishing act. I could break off all my London ties and pack
in time to fly to the Bahamas at once.'

Olly looked at her quickly. 'So soon, you think?'

'It seems as well.'

Olly looked down at her plate. 'It's up to you. I
should be very happy to have you here for the rest of
the week, my dear.'

'I've enjoyed it very much, but I think I would like
to get things settled in London. I must see my cousin
and talk to him. He'll have to get another job.'

'Will that be difficult for him?' Olly frowned.

Rachel shook her head. 'He's a good pianist. He's
had offers before. He does session work with a record-
ing company, in fact, when he feels like it.'

'It sounds fascinating.' Olly pushed back her chair.
'If you do decide to go, I'll have a car ready to take you
whenever you want it.'

Rachel drew a deep breath. 'At eleven, then? It will
take me a little while to pack.'

Olly looked at her, her brows level. 'Very well,
Rachel. I'm very happy to have met you. I hope we'll
meet again before too long.'

Rachel smiled and Olly went out. When she had
finished her breakfast Rachel went up to her room and
packed. At eleven the car stood outside the house. She
said goodbye again to Olly and was firmly kissed on
both cheeks, then she sat back and refused to look as
Ambreys rapidly glided out of sight.

She stared out of the window at the green countryside. She would never see Mark Hammond again and
she had to learn to be thankful for that. No matter
how long it took to school herself to feel it.

CHAPTER SEVEN

DERRY was inexplicably terse when they met for lunch next day. Rachel thought at first that it was her own news which had angered him, but she soon saw that something else was on his mind. Derry was disturbed about something, but it had nothing to do with her.

'Of course I don't object,' he said when she told him of the offer of a job in the Bahamas.

'You don't?' Rachel sounded as surprised as she felt.

Derry grimaced, catching the note in her voice. 'Let me re-phrase that, baby. I'll miss you, but I won't stand in your way. I can get a job without you, Ray—I've had offers enough in the past.'

'I remember.' Rachel smiled at him. 'You're good, Derry. I'm sure you won't lack work. But after our long partnership I felt guilty about going.'

'Why should you?' Derry had flushed, his eyes not quite meeting her own. Was she imagining it or had a look of consciousness spread over his face for a moment? 'We've been together a long time, but we aren't Siamese twins, for heaven's sake.'

'I'm glad you see it like that.'

'I hope you have a success over there.' He met her eyes then, smiling at her. 'You deserve it.' His manner brightened. 'And all that sunshine, those beaches— what a place to work! You'll have a great time, Ray.'

'I'm going to work!' But she smiled as she retorted quickly, 'All the same, I am looking forward to seeing the Bahamas, I admit.'

Derry's face grew sharp, almost savage. 'So the Hammonds won? They finally got rid of you? And cheaply, at that.'

Her face tightened and went pink. 'They didn't buy me of, Derry! In fact, Mark Hammond had nothing to do with it. He doesn't even know where I'm going. His mother set it up for me and she did it with the utmost tact; there was no suggestion of bribery. We both agreed that I had to get out of Nicky's way until he was over me.'

Derry nodded cynically. 'Oh, clever. What Mark couldn't do, his mother managed in her own way.' His eyes watched her. 'You say he doesn't know you're going to the Bahamas?'

'Mrs Hammond promised not to tell him.'

'You believed her?'

Rachel met his eyes. 'Implicitly. You haven't met her. She's honest, Derry, I'd swear to it. I liked her.'

Derry looked maliciously at her. 'You liked Mark too, didn't you?'

Her colour deepened and she felt her mouth tremble. Looking away, she said huskily, 'That's not very kind, Derry.'

He muttered something under his breath and put an arm round her. 'I ought to be shot. I'm sorry, Ray. Forget I said a word. And if Mark Hammond comes here looking for you I'll show him the door.'

'Thank you,' she said, her face blank. Derry did not yet know just how nasty Mark Hammond could be. She had no illusions as to the tactics Mark could employ if he was determined to find her, but she knew he would not try. She had gone. That would satisfy him. Nicky would be safe.

She flew to the Bahamas next day. Derry saw her off
at the airport. Just before she walked away from him
he hugged her, whispering, 'Don't worry, baby, I'm
going to give the Hammonds and their friends the hell
of a shock. They'll pay for what they did to you.'

Rachel was alarmed and puzzled. She looked at him
anxiously. 'What?'

He kissed her and pushed her through the gate.
'You'll miss your plane!'

The last departures were moving through. Derry was
right; she had no time to linger, questioning him. She
went, but looked back in a worried way, a frown on her
face. Derry waved, then vanished into the moving
throng of passengers.

On the flight Rachel stared from the window at the
ceaseless flow of the sky. What had he meant? What
was he up to?

Derry had always been a gambler, in all senses of
the word, risking far too much merely for the thrill of
it. She hoped desperately that he had not got himself
involved in anything illegal. He had been behaving in
an odd way for some time now. There had been a few
other cryptic remarks, little hints, hard to pin down but
recurring often enough to alert her.

He had a zany streak in his make-up. Unpredictable,
he was capable of any nonsense, particularly if he saw
a way of making money. He had no scruples to restrain
him. Only Rachel's affection for him had ever held him
back in the past. Now they seemed to have drifted too
far apart from each other for him to be prepared to
listen to her.

It had not occurred to her that there would be a
time change during her flight. She had left early in the

morning, warned that the flight took over six hours.
They were served lunch on the plane, the usual card-
board airline food in a plastic tray, and by the time
they arrived Rachel felt wearily that she had been in
transit for days. Glancing at her watch, she realised she
had not wound it back four hours, and that in island
time it was now lunchtime, although she had eaten
lunch a long time ago.

It was an unsettling thought. Around her the other
passengers were resetting their watches and she exchanged smiles with the woman sitting beside her.

When she had been through Customs she heard her
own name being called on the tannoy and made her
way to the flight reception desk. A man in a peaked cap
and white shorts was waiting for her, a broad smile
on his dark face.

'Miss Austen? I'm the driver from the Orioca. Welcome to the island. Let me take that bag.'

She followed him out into the sunshine, her eyes
lifting to the blue sky, aware at once of the alien atmosphere, the impression of somnolent ease around her.
Everything looked strange to her, but she had no time
to do more than drink in the briefest glimpse before
she was seated in the back of the car and speeding
away.

'Mr MacIntyre said you was from London,' the driver
remarked over his broad shoulder. 'A good flight, was
it?'

'Tiring,' Rachel confessed, smiling as she caught the
white flash of his teeth.

'Come to sing?' He was taking his time, driving ex-
pertly but without haste along the dusty white road.
Rachel gazed at the thick green tropical-looking trees

which she could not identify, their lush growth giving
welcome shade to pedestrians who sauntered along in
bright cotton clothing.

'Yes,' she admitted, glancing at the driver's curly
black hair as it straggled from beneath his cap.

He made light, friendly conversation all the way to
the club and she responded in kind, liking his easy
manner and cheerful smile.

'You'll like Mr MacIntyre.' He flashed those white
teeth at her again, turning his head to do so. 'Everybody likes Mr MacIntyre, particularly the ladies.'

'Sounds ominous!' Rachel's voice was dry.

The driver laughed deeply. 'No, ma'am. He's a nice
man, a really nice man. If you're ever in trouble you
can trust Mr MacIntyre.'

'I hope I never am,' Rachel returned wryly.

The driver waved a large black hand to the left.
'We're here.'

She looked through the belt of close-set trees and saw
the new white building with a gleam of bright blue at
its foot, the rawness of its novelty softened by palms
and flowering shrubs, green lawns and flower beds.

As the car drew up a man stepped through the double
glass doors and opened the door to help her alight. She
straightened to find herself held by the hand firmly.
Brown eyes smiled into her own.

'Miss Austen? I'm Ian MacIntyre. Welcome to the
Orioca and to the island.'

Rachel smiled back at him. 'Hallo! Thanks for
the welcome. I can't tell you how relieved I am to be
standing on firm land after that flight. I felt quite
seasick when I got off the plane.'

Ian MacIntyre laughed. 'You look just fine.' His

eyes roamed over her in an entirely friendly way. 'Olly said you were lovely, but I'm beginning to think she underestimated. If you sing as well as she claims I'll be overjoyed.'

'Thank you.' She glanced down at her trapped hand. 'Any chance of getting my hand back? I'm not ambidextrous!'

He grinned, releasing her. 'Sorry—I was carried away. Come on to your chalet.' He put a hand beneath her elbow, turning her away from the white building. 'We all live in chalets; it makes for more privacy and a chance of a rest on our days off. The club is open seven days a week, but you won't have to work on Sundays, unless there's a private function where you've accepted a booking, and that's entirely up to you. The club doesn't take a cut for private functions, by the way. If you want to sing off duty, that's your affair.'

'You're the manager?'

He nodded. 'Manager and owner.'

'Oh.' Rachel looked sideways at him in some surprise. His casual friendliness had not given her the impression that he was wealthy, yet the owner of the Orioca must certainly be quite well off.

Ian MacIntyre gave her a smile. 'Part-owner, actually. Olly has a quarter share.'

Rachel was surprised again. 'She has?'

'She didn't tell you?'

Rachel shook her head. Olly had told her very little, she thought. What had she told Ian MacIntyre? How much of the story did he know? He was giving nothing away, his manner perfectly easy with her.

'Has Mark Hammond anything to do with the club?' She managed to keep her voice level, watching Ian.

'Mark?' Ian grinned. 'Not on your life! I wouldn't cut that shark in on a deal, Miss Austen. Mark's like woodworm. Get it in one place and the next thing you know, the whole place is riddled with it.'

She laughed, somehow convinced that Olly had kept her secret. Ian halted beside a one-storey little white building framed in palms and unlocked the door, handing her the key with a ceremonial bow. 'Your home for the next few months, Miss Austen.' Glancing over his shoulder he said, 'And here's Benny with the bags, so you could unpack right now if you felt like it, although if I were you I'd postpone that until you'd had a short sleep followed by a late lunch.'

'I ate on the plane.'

Benny carried the bags through into the cool, white-painted little room and Rachel followed, glancing around with interest. The chalet was divided into three—a sitting-room with a tiny kitchenette at one end of it, a small bedroom and a bathroom. Ian MacIntyre walked round, throwing open the doors, inviting her to inspect the rooms.

'I'm overwhelmed,' she said lightly. 'It's lovely.'

There was a minimum of modern furniture and the rooms were light and attractive, spacious in design, although the floor space was obviously limited.

Benny moved to the door and she called a grateful, 'Thank you, Benny,' as he went out. He turned and grinned, lifting a hand.

Ian MacIntyre was watching her when she turned. 'You've got a beautiful name,' he said. 'Rachel Austen. Is it real? Or did you pick it out of a hat?'

'It's real,' she laughed. 'I was born with it, or rather given it at birth.'

'Rachel . . .' He murmured the name softly. 'May I

call you that? Or do you prefer formality between
working companions?'

'Rachel suits me fine,' she said.

'And Ian suits me,' he returned, his brown eyes
twinkling. He moved to the door. 'Have a rest, then
come over to the club to have dinner. It's usually at
eight-thirty to nine-thirty for staff, but as you're out
of step time-wise you can eat whenever you get hungry.
The kitchen will make you up a salad and some fish
or steak.'

'Thank you.' She stood there, her slim rounded body
weary, her eyes shadowed with more than the ex-
haustion of the journey. Ian gave her a quick, shrewd
look from her bright rich hair to her slim legs.

'You'll feel better in the morning. It takes a day to
get over jet lag.'

'When do I start work?'

He laughed. 'Give yourself time to get acclimatised!
I'll hear you tomorrow morning, get an idea of what
you can do, then we'll discuss your schedule and you
can meet the other artistes. I've got a group, a few
dancers and a comedian. We do a full-scale show most
nights. We get a lot of customers.'

When he had closed the door Rachel slumped, turning to face the bright little room. She felt odd. A few
days ago she was at Ambreys in the depth of the English countryside and now she was many miles away on
the other side of the world. It had happened too soon
and she was caught in a frenetic time drag which left
her giddy, totally disorientated.

Stepping out of her shoes, she curled up on the neat
white bed. Her eyes closed with relief. Within minutes
she was asleep.

When she opened her eyes again it was dark. There was a faint sound of music somewhere, voices laughing, the swish of tyres on gravel and the rustle of branches against the walls of her chalet. Lying in the velvety darkness she listened, pinning all the sounds down, trying to make herself believe where she was and what she was doing.

At last she got up and went over to the window, closing the blinds. The movement shut out the pale glimmer of light which had crept into the room. Quickly she switched on the light and the little white room flashed on to her sight.

She walked into the bathroom, stripped and had a warm shower, then chose a lime green dress and quickly slid into it.

Ten minutes later she found her way to the clubhouse and went in through the double doors. In the blue-tiled foyer an old man sat at a desk reading a newspaper. He lowered it and gave her a faint nod.

'Good evening,' Rachel said nervously. 'I . . .'

Her words broke off as Ian MacIntyre walked through a swing door and gave her a smile. 'You look better. Good sleep?'

'Very good,' Rachel told him. 'So good it's left me starving!'

'You don't surprise me! It's nearly nine. You must be ravenous.' He took her bare arm in one hand. 'Come on, I'll show you the staff table in the dining-room.'

The elegant, spacious dining-room was filled with people, talking, laughing, eating beautifully prepared and served meals. Ian guided her across the room to a large table at which a trio of men sat talking and drinking coffee.

'Rachel, these are Brad West, our comedian; Tony Carter, one of our group Horse, and another of the group, the drummer in fact, Peter Singledge.'

The men looked at her with appraising interest and she smiled around the table.

'Ian forgot to mention I'm not only lead guitarist, I sing,' Tony said, his skinny shoulders hunched. 'Not that it matters. I'm a rotten singer, I admit it.'

Peter's sandy eyebrows flicked towards her, his eyes smiling. 'In case you need a translation, you just heard envy and fury in his voice. Tony doesn't need to hear you sing to know you're going to knock spots off him.'

Tony growled into his coffee cup.

Peter patted him kindly on his shoulder. 'Bear up, Tony. You can't help it if you aren't a beautiful, slinky redhead.'

'My hair is not red,' Rachel said firmly.

Peter eyed it. 'I must get my eyes fixed.'

'Chestnut,' she said. 'My hair is chestnut.'

'Like my jokes,' Brad West chimed in, his rough voice wry.

Peter mimed the strumming of a guitar. 'That was a sample of his jokes,' he told Rachel. 'Now you've been warned. He borrowed them from the *Beano*.'

'They didn't want them.' Brad eyed Rachel, his leer deliberate and jokey. 'But I could want you, Miss Austen. My chalet or yours?'

Rachel sweetly smiled back. 'Well, I'd love that, Brad, but it's my friend ... he goes green and shoots up to thirty foot if I so much as smile at another man.'

'The Incredible Hulk's your boy-friend?' He snapped his fingers. 'So that's why he's been lurking in the undergrowth today.'

'Stupid, that was Tony,' Peter retorted. He was a slim, pleasant boy of twenty or so with fair hair and blue eyes. Brad was a good ten years older, his thin brown hair combed carefully over his temples. Between them, Tony looked like a skinny teenager, but at close quarters his face looked much older, sharper, more knowledgeable, although he had a depressed, sullen expression when he was not speaking.

Rachel's steak and salad arrived and she ate it while Tony and the others argued. After a while they drifted off and Ian talked to her about the club, explaining the way it worked. It offered a wide range of sporting activities from skin-diving to deep-sea fishing, with the usual tennis, squash and swimming thrown in at the club grounds. There was a good beach just five minutes across the grounds. Members could use it freely and had free access to the beach equipment kept in the club. In the evenings there were plenty of activities; a restaurant, bars, disco and nightclub.

'We cater for a variety of people, Rachel, and we like to think we give them their money's worth, whatever it is they want to do. When you aren't working, which includes a daily rehearsal of course, you're free to go where you please and use any part of the club, any equipment, so long as you've informed the club secretary what you're doing. We like to be sure you aren't putting yourself at risk in the sea, using equipment you're not expert with, you see. Once we're sure you can be trusted not to kill yourself, we can relax.'

She nodded. 'I'll remember.'

'Any sport you particularly fancy?'

'Skin-diving,' she said eagerly.

He laughed. 'Good swimmer?'

She shrugged. 'Fair.'

'You've got to be better than fair if you want to dive.' Ian's face was serious. 'I'll take you out myself before I let you loose. You must never dive alone, though, always with a group. Too much can happen to you when you're down there, and I don't want to lose my new singer.'

Rachel smiled. 'I'll be careful, I promise.'

Having finished her coffee, she pushed away the cup and gazed around her. The room was slowly emptying and the sound of music was louder. 'The group is well under way,' Ian said drily. 'Do you like pop?'

'Depends on the sort. This is tuneful.'

'Give Pete a set of drums and he can ruin your hearing for life,' Ian grimaced. 'When he's in a temper he smashes hell out of his drums.'

Rachel laughed. 'I rather liked him. Tony seemed a little off key, though.'

Ian looked amused. 'He's off women at the moment. A dose of unrequited love has left him in a cynical mood.'

'Oh, dear.' Rachel smiled back. 'Poor Tony!'

'She was a tourist—it was one of those brief romances which leave a scar. She flew off back to the States and Tony went into a deep decline. I expect he'll pull out of it.'

He seemed a level-headed, pleasant man, his face strong and reliable, his voice calm and easy on the ear. Rachel sensed she was going to like him, to find it easy to get on with him. After the bitterness of her relationship with Mark Hammond it was a relief to be with a man who talked to one as if one were a human being, not an object.

He walked back to her chalet with her. The sleepy
warmth of the night lay over the club grounds like a
velvet canopy, the skies deep and darkly brilliant. Ian
paused outside her chalet and looked into her face.

'I hope you're going to be happy with us, Rachel.
I've got a feeling you're going to be a success with our
customers. You've a warm personality and the sort of
looks which are striking without being lurid—we've
had problems before now with girls who are out here
to grab themselves either money or a man. I don't feel
you're going to fit into that category.' The brown eyes
had a hard glint suddenly. 'I hope so, anyway.'

Rachel gave him a slight smile. 'You don't need to
underline the warning. I get the point.'

His eyes softened. 'I'm sure you do, and I'm sure I
had no need to give you a warning. You aren't that
sort of girl.'

'I'm just here to work.' She opened her chalet and
switched on the light. It fell over the narrow, grass-
trimmed path in a yellow swathe.

Ian nodded. 'Goodnight, Rachel. I'll hear you at
ten o'clock tomorrow. I would like to see your wardrobe, too, if you don't mind. I like to pass every item
personally, and that includes clothes.'

'Of course.' She moved into the chalet, glancing
back at him. 'Goodnight.'

He moved off and she shut the door, sighing as she
leaned against it. She was feeling tired again. The
narrow white bed looked very inviting.

A few moments later the light was out and she was
falling into a deep sleep again.

By the vivid sunlight of the morning the club
grounds offered a strange, alien beauty to the eye;

bougainvillaea climbing in thick hedges everywhere, the bright tropical colours dazzling, hibiscus holding yellow stamens to the visiting butterflies, heady-scented flowers giving the deep green of the grass an unreal quality. There were white chalets scattered at intervals among the trees on this side of the club. On the other the gardens stretched down to a sea so blue and so clear that it looked artificial. A swimming pool lay beside the white building, some guests splashing in the bright water. Striped beach umbrellas fluttered in a faint breeze above the round white tables at which some people sat sipping long drinks decorated like hats with fruit and green leaves.

Rachel had woken early and strolled around taking in her new surroundings. By the time she joined Ian at the club she was beginning to feel she knew her way around.

Ian leaned back in the shadows of the club, his face invisible, the drawn blinds giving the room a coolness which she was to find very attractive after she had been in the island a few days. Blue shade lay in pools on the parquet floor. Bright golden streams of sunshine tumbled between them. From the pool outside she heard splashes, cries and laughter.

Peter played for her, his hands deft and accustomed. She sang to him, rather than to Ian, on instinct, and he grinned at her as he played, enjoying their partner-ship. When Ian stood up she jerked her head round to look almost nervously at him.

He strolled up and kissed her teasingly on the nose. 'I must write and thank Olly. She's found me a jewel.'

Rachel let out a long sigh of relief.

Ian's brows lifted. 'You weren't nervous?'

'Horribly!'

'My dear girl, you're too good to feel like that. How long did you say you'd been singing?'

'Since I was sixteen, but that makes no difference. Every time I go on it's like the first time. I feel sick as I walk out in front of an audience.'

'Well, our audience is going to love you.' He was firm about that, his smile amused.

'I'll say!' Peter crashed his hands down on the piano. 'Poor old Tony—are his eyes going to be green!'

'It will make no difference to Tony.' Ian looked wry. 'Or it shouldn't do. He has his own audience. In his way, he can be quite effective.'

On her first evening at the club Rachel was tense with nerves, her skin pale, her eyes over-bright. Ian put an arm around her and gave her a calming smile. 'Hey, unwind! And that's an order.'

'Yes, Boss.' She smiled back at him, liking him enormously. She had already realised that everybody liked him, from the kitchen staff to the gloomy Tony. Ian had a quiet, reliable, honest face. It was easy to trust him. He had authority, but he masked it with kindness. People did not argue with Ian MacIntyre. They listened and they smiled and they did what he asked.

He was, in his way, a man with as much magnetism as Mark Hammond, but it was of a very different order.

Her first appearance was a great success. Ian looked pleased and triumphant as he kissed her afterwards. 'I knew you would be a hit!' He ordered champagne and the others laughingly raised their glasses to her as they sipped the dry, bubbly liquid.

Within a few weeks Rachel felt she was at home in

the club. She began to slip into a daily pattern which suited her. Unlike some of the others she preferred to go to bed early in order to get up early and go down to the beach before any of their members arrived. The empty, untouched loveliness of the sands, the blue of the sea, the cry of the seabirds, made each morning a delight. She had never lived in such a beautiful place. After London it was a little like heaven.

After a light quick breakfast she sometimes went into the little town nearby with Ian. He personally inspected the food bought for the club, showing as much interest in the lobster, crab and other seafood as he did in the acts he engaged for the nightly cabaret.

Seafood was the chef's speciality, although just as many guests ate steak. He insisted on the freshest ingredients and Ian liked to keep an eye on the quality and price of them.

Within a short time of her arrival, Rachel had bought herself a new wardrobe of beach wear, partly at Ian's suggestion.

'Although your show clothes are the most important, it's also important for you to look lovely off duty. Many of our guests will see you on the beach and around the town, so you must look special whenever you walk out of your chalet.'

He had come along with her, viewed the swimwear and shorts she chose, advised her on the colours and styles he thought she should wear. His attention to every tiny detail was impressive but a little alarming.

'Is he always so meticulous?' she asked Pete.

The two of them had drifted into a close, easy friendship without any sexual hang-up. Peter had a girlfriend in England, he had confided, to whom he wrote three times a week, and although he flirted at times with pretty girls he met in the club, he kept himself strictly to himself off duty, preferring not to get involved.

'I want to marry Ann,' he told her. 'There could never be anyone else for me.'

Now he answered her thoughtfully, 'Ian doesn't miss a thing, but I think he rather fancies you, Ray.' Pete eyed her quizzically. 'How about you?'

Rachel flushed. His reply had taken her aback. It had never entered her head.

'I . . . hadn't thought about it.'

Pete whistled softly, eyes interested. 'Poor old Ian!'

He said no more and neither did Rachel, but the conversation had given her a new view of Ian and the next time they met she gave him a secret, careful look, but saw no sign of any clue to back up Peter's suspicions.

It was clear that Ian liked her, but no more than he liked everybody he employed. His manner to her was as calmly friendly as it was to the other members of staff.

Peter, she decided, had been indulging his imagination, and the conviction made her relax again. The last thing she had wanted was to have any emotional entanglement while she was in the island. She was enjoying her stay at the club. Her career would not be harmed by having spent some months singing in a famous holiday island and she enjoyed the lazy, light-hearted atmosphere in which she now worked. The sunshine and sea air seemed to make people far more relaxed, draining away the tension she had sometimes encountered in London.

Olly had kept her word. Rachel had several chatty, characteristic letters from her, from which she discovered that Nicky had been deeply upset by her disappearance but had settled down again in time. At present, Olly said, he was working very hard with his studies and showing a new interest in them. He was also occasionally seeing Jane Palfrey. They quarrelled violently, but Nicky went on seeing her, so Olly drew the conclusion that he was not indifferent to her, although they spent most of their time together shouting and sniping at each other.

There was no mention of Mark's reaction to Rachel's vanishing act. The only time Olly mentioned his name was when she said that he had returned to the States, leaving Nicky in London.

That was that, Rachel had thought, reading the brief sentence. The incident was over. All she had to do now was forget she had ever met him, and that she was fiercely determined to do.

Her replies to Olly were as lightly chatty, full of tiny snippets about her life on the island, descriptions of the scenery and amused references to Ian's paternalistic tyranny of them all.

She had been at the club for eight weeks when Ian asked her to sing at a private function he was organising. A willowy, dark-skinned girl with brown eyes who often came to the club was just twenty-one and was having a celebration in the club on a Sunday evening. After Rachel had sung she was invited to join the party. Ian danced with her several times, his eyes smiling as they circled the floor. He walked with her to her chalet later and before he said goodnight kissed her.

It was the first time he had done so, and the kiss told

her several things which startled and disturbed her. Pete had not been entirely wrong about Ian's interest in her, she realised. The hard kiss had been very personal.

Disturbed, she lay awake for some time, worrying about it. She did not want Ian to move beyond the calm friendship she had thought they shared. He had said nothing she could object to—he had given her no chance of making her feelings clear, walking away as soon as he had released her. What could she do to show him that she had no interest in him outside friendship?

CHAPTER EIGHT

DERRY was not a frequent correspondent. His letters came at rare intervals, usually brief notes excusing himself for not having written before, giving her a few short glimpses of his life and how his career was going. He had managed to get quite a few jobs since they split up, but although he seemed pleased with how things were going he appeared to be more interested in something else. Rachel was not sure what was on his mind, but she suspected he had some plan which he was pursuing. It bothered her, but with half the world between them she had no chance to probe beneath his light tone.

During the ninth week she spent on the island she got another of his short letters, and a casual reference to the Hammonds disturbed her. Derry was still clearly brooding over the way she had been treated. He had been visiting his parents, she discovered. Derry rarely saw them, although they were deeply attached to him, and it pleased her that he had been home.

The same week she got a letter from her aunt, Derry's mother, and a phrase about 'Derry's girl' sent a wave of alarm through her. She sat staring at the words. What girl? Derry had not breathed a word of any girl-friend to her. Women came and went in his life, but none of them had ever stayed more than a few days and certainly none of them had ever been taken to meet his family.

She knew better than to ask him. If he wanted her to know, he would have told her. Sighing, she folded both letters away together and forgot about it for the moment.

Ian had taken her skin-diving several times before relinquishing her to the tender care of their expert, a thin, tough young man who had been born on the island and loved the water, spending most of his time in it when he was not lying sun-basking on the beach.

The day after she got the letter from Derry's mother, Ian invited her to dive with him. 'I want to see how you're getting on, Rachel. I've had excellent reports from Joe.' His eyes twinkled. 'But I would like to see for myself how much of the hyperbole is based on fact and how much of it is due to your big green eyes and sexy figure.'

Rachel flushed slightly. 'Joe knows what he's talking about.'

Ian's brow lifted steeply. 'Does he?'

She flushed more deeply, then laughed. 'You know what I mean.'

He grinned. 'Of course I do, but you take the bait so delightfully. I enjoy making you blush.'

'I wish you wouldn't.' She gave him a firm look. 'It isn't very kind.'

Ian looked down at her thoughtfully. 'I could be very kind to you, Rachel. You make it easy.'

She turned away, embarrassed by his expression and tone. Hurrying to her chalet, she changed into a one-piece white bathing suit and tied her hair deftly into a knot at the back of her head. Collecting her diving gear from the club, she joined Ian and they walked down to the beach.

She had already learnt how to dive gracefully and as silently as possible to the sea-bed, and how to relax so that her body should not use up air too quickly, prolonging the length of time she could thus spend under water. She had been enchanted by the mysterious green-blue world she glimpsed under the waves, feeling her limp body trailing without resistance as she felt her way over the sandy sea-bed.

Ian watched her, his own technique flawless, his body powerful as he moved beside her in the sea.

When they surfaced together, his arm around her waist, on their third trip down, he smiled at her, still holding her close. 'Joe didn't exaggerate. You're very promising for a beginner.'

She sparkled with pleasure, smiling into his brown eyes. 'Why, thank you! How long have you been diving?' She was too interested in his answer, too pleased by his compliment, to note the calm assurance of his hold on her, the way his hand splayed out over her wet midriff.

'I can't even remember.' Ian laughed. 'My first few dives were pretty hair-raising, though. I was too keen and I spent too long down there. By the time I came up I was having trouble breathing. I blacked out a couple of times and after that I'd learnt my lesson.'

'It must have been terrifying.'

'It was, at the time, but later I was grateful for the warnings. I learnt never to stay down until my air was already too low for safety.' He looked into her eyes soberly. 'Don't forget that, Rachel. Always surface before the danger level is reached.'

Very seriously she looked up into his face and nodded. 'Don't worry, Joe has hammered that into my head. I don't take risks.'

He smiled, his face charming. 'I'm glad to hear that. I would hate anything to happen to you just as we were getting to know each other.' His hand moved up to touch her cheek very lightly.

She became aware then of the intimacy of their closeness and froze, moving away.

Ian dropped his hand, staring at her. Rachel gave him a rather nervous smile, turning to walk through the water to the beach. The sands were quite crowded with people, mainly sunbathing on loungers. A few people were throwing a ball to and fro, a girl was turning cartwheels, her blue bikini precarious as she turned round. There were even a few who wore no clothes at all, stretched out totally nude on the sand. The club ignored this practice unless someone complained, when the offender would be asked politely to desist.

Collecting her gear together, Rachel waited on the sand for Ian to join her, her eye roving casually over the throng. It halted abruptly and her heart stopped. It had not done that since the last time she saw Mark Hammond, but it did it now, face to face with him across the pale yellow sands.

He was standing framed by palm trees on the edge of the beach, his lithe body casually dressed in white slacks and a black shirt open at the neck.

Across the heads of the sunbathers they stared at each other. Rachel thought for a long moment that he was a figment of her imagination, the product of a mirage-like dream.

'Ready?'

Ian had come up behind her and was sliding his arm around her back, glancing into her fixed face.

She started, turning to him. 'Oh, yes,' she stammered, and he gave her a quick, shrewd glance.

'Look, Rachel, there's no need to get worked up about anything,' he said gently. 'Take things as they come. I'm in no hurry. I just enjoy your company—there are no strings.'

Her colour rose and she gave him a nervous smile. 'I understand.' She looked round and was torn between regret and delight to find Mark still there. He was not a mirage. He was really on the island, watching them with a cold, dark face, obviously waiting for them to walk towards him.

Ian moved and she fell into step, staring at her own feet. What was Mark doing here? Had Olly informed him of her whereabouts? Or had he done some checking of his own? It could, of course, be a complete coincidence that he was here. He might have flown to the island for a holiday or to check on his mother's investment in Ian's club.

Ian made a startled noise and she looked up anxiously. 'Good lord!' His face split with a wry smile. He was staring at Mark who now strolled forward to meet them. 'What are you doing over here?'

'A quick trip on business,' said Mark, and the deep, cold note of his voice was horribly familiar. It sent a shiver down her spine.

Ian held out a hand and Mark shook it with a brief but perceptible hesitation which made Ian look at him in question.

Slowly Mark's blue eyes moved to Rachel.

Ian politely began to introduce them. 'This is your mother's protégée, Rachel Austen.'

Mark made no attempt to offer his hand. His eyes were chips of blue ice. He inclined his head. 'We've met.'

The brief, curt reply had the effect of an insult and her colour rose. She was too angry to speak, her eyes flaring.

Ian looked from one to the other, his brows sharply lifted. 'I see,' he drawled, and Rachel wondered what he saw and hoped it was not too clearly.

Suddenly there was a scream from the beach and Ian's head swung round as the sound of splashing and shouting came from the water. 'A shark, a shark!'

'What the devil . . .' Ian dropped his gear and raced off while Rachel and Mark stared after him. In the blue water the dark triangular fin was already causing panic among the sunbathers and swimmers, but in another moment there was laughter and angry murmurs as it became clear that it was a practical joke. Ian emerged from the water, his hand fiercely dragging a teenage boy by the ear. A black rubber fin was strapped to his skinny body, and at once some of the women reacted with the irritation of those who have been badly frightened.

Rachel watched the little crowd gathering around Ian and his companion, heard Ian's calming, propitiating voice.

Mark's hand descended on her arm and she swung, startled, to look at him.

'We have some talking to do,' Mark muttered through his teeth.

She glanced back towards Ian, but he was surrounded by people and too deeply involved to catch her eye. Mark followed her gaze and his fingers tightened, hurting her.

'We're going to talk without an audience,' he said brusquely, starting to walk away and pulling her with him.

'Ian will wonder where I've got to!'

'Tough!' Mark was walking fast now and she had to run to keep up with him, her arm still held in that iron grip.

'I have to change! I'm wet.'

'Where's your chalet?'

They were crossing the smooth green lawns now and she forced him to stop, her heels digging in, her face mulish. 'I'll see you in the club later.'

'You think I'd let you skip off again?' He looked derisively at her. 'Thank you, sweetheart. You must think I'm a fool. I've caught up with you now and you're staying caught.'

'Where the hell am I supposed to go on this island?' Her temper flared, her eyes dark green.

'You might fly off somewhere. Who knows? I've learnt my lesson. I'm sticking at your side until I get some answers out of you.'

He looked capable of anything, his face harsh, and she was scared of him. Lowering her head, she let him pull her on again, saying in a quiet voice, 'My chalet is the third one on the right.'

The blinds were half down in the chalet, giving the room a cool greeny shadow which was refreshing after the sunlight. The fan whirred softly overhead. Mark watched her dispose of her gear, his hands in his pockets.

'I won't be a moment,' she said crisply, pulling a white shift out of the wardrobe and walking into the bathroom.

She showered quickly to rid herself of salt on her skin, dressed and went back into the other room. Mark stood at the window, his black head outlined against the criss-cross shadows from the blind.

He turned and looked her up and down. 'Your skin looks ravishing with that sun-tan,' he said almost impersonally.

The sun had gradually given her a golden hue which she now barely noticed herself. Against the straight white of the thin dress she looked slender and glowingly healthy.

She had brushed her hair into its usual full style. The sun had altered the colour of that too, giving her far more golden lights, leaving the shade richer and more burnished.

'Shall we go over to the club? I'm afraid I don't have a drink for you.'

He glanced at the electric kettle. 'No coffee?'

'Oh, of course,' she said, moving into the tiny kitchenette. 'I meant whisky.'

'Coffee will do fine.'

He moved over to join her, leaning on the end of the unit top, his elbow propping his dark head. She moved around getting the coffee, very aware of him watching her.

She passed him a cup of coffee and he took it, walking with it to the two chairs beside the coffee table. Rachel followed with her own cup and sat down, placing her cup on the low glass-topped table.

Her eyes on the blue shadows creeping across the floor, she asked, 'How did you know I was here?'

'Olly,' he said shortly.

She looked up, her mouth tight. 'She promised not to tell you!'

Mark's eyes were dark. 'She kept her promise until I had to know.'

Rachel stared briefly, then looked away. 'Why did you have to know?'

He laughed curtly. 'You don't know?'

She shook her head.

'Come off it,' Mark said tersely, his face dangerous.

She looked up then, frowning. 'We're talking at cross-purposes. Could you start again?'

He watched her. 'I'm talking about your cousin Derry.'

She tensed, her muscles tight. Her eyes met his anxiously. 'What has Derry done?'

She had not known that it was Derry who had brought Mark in search of her, but she was not surprised. She had been expecting Derry to do something, although she had no idea what it was she feared.

Mark watched her coldly. 'He didn't keep you informed?'

She linked her hands tightly. 'Please! Just tell me!'

Mark's mouth hardened. 'He's run off with little Julia Brennan, Graham Brennan's only offspring, and I don't have to tell you what a fuss her father is making! He has men scouring the country looking for them, but your dear cousin has made sure of leaving no clues. I've been down to see his family, but they know nothing.' His eyes held hers, his face angry. 'So! I had to know what you could tell me. And make no mistake about it, Rachel, you will tell me, sooner or later.'

Rachel was pale and disturbed. 'I don't know anything about it. Derry hasn't mentioned it to me.' Her eyes were wide, anxious. 'He knew better than to tell me. I couldn't possibly encourage him to do such a thing.' She knew that Julia Brennan was only seventeen, a child with more money than was good for her, one of Nicky's friends, a spoilt and silly child but

nevertheless still a child. She would have stopped
Derry if she had known anything about it, and Derry
had known it.

Mark's mouth drew in tightly. 'You expect me to believe that?' He smiled coldly, ferociously. 'We'll find
him, you know, and when we do he'll get the book
thrown at him. Her father has had her made a ward of
court. She's under age, she can't marry without per-
mission.' His eyes were savage. 'And if your cousin has
seduced her he'll pay for that, too.'

Rachel leapt to her feet and Mark stood up too, moving to catch hold of her arm. She shook herself free
angrily. 'I'm going to show you his letters, that's all.'

He watched as she went to the little drawer, pulled
out the pile of letters from Derry and his parents,
showed them to him. Mark took them, sat down and
began to read, his black head bent, his face hard.

There was a knock at the door. Mark looked up and
his eyes were warily dark.

Rachel went to open the door. Ian looked past her
and his face registered nothing as he saw Mark with
the letters in his hand, saw the cold offhand expression
of his face.

'You haven't checked the gear back into the clubhouse,' Ian said quietly.

His eyes searched her face and she gave him an
apologetic, unhappy smile.

'I'm sorry. I was going to do that later,' she said.

'I'll do it for you,' said Ian, walking past her and
retrieving the gear. Mark returned to his perusal of
the letters, but Rachel sensed that he was aware of
Ian's movements, his attention not held by what he
was reading.

Ian glanced at Mark. 'Can I have a word alone, Rachel?' he asked as he moved back to the door.

Mark's head was thrown back, his eyes watching as she stepped out of the chalet and Ian deliberately closed the door. The sunlight was brilliant, hurting her eyes. She watched the lazy movement of the palm leaves in the faint breeze. A vivid butterfly skimmed over the unreal, tropical flowers which spilled in bright colours over the wall nearby.

'Is anything wrong?' Ian asked gently, watching her averted face.

She smiled at him with an effort. 'A personal matter.'

Ian watched carefully, his eyes probing. 'I didn't realise you knew Mark Hammond personally.'

Her colour darkened and she looked away. 'I met him a few times.' She looked back at him, almost pleadingly. 'He wants my help over something to do with a relative of mine.' She did not want him to ask too many questions and her eyes gave that away.

His brows drew together. 'Then there's something wrong.'

Rachel sighed. 'I'm afraid so, but nothing you can help with, Ian. In fact, it's nothing to do with me, except that ...' She broke off, suddenly aware of a shadow behind the blinds in her chalet. Mark was listening, watching. The realisation made her tremble, her face off balance.

Ian caught the unguarded movement, the misery in her eyes, and he pushed his free arm around her, pulling her closer. His lips brushed her hair. 'Anything I can do to help, Rachel, you know you only have to ask.'

She stood without pushing him away, half leaning on him, grateful for his strength and gentleness. 'Thank you, Ian. You're so kind.'

He laughed wryly. 'I wish you hadn't said that.'

Her eyes opened wide, puzzled. 'Why?'

He slid his hand up to her chin, tilting her face. 'My dear girl, it's practically an insult!' His face was self-derisive. He bent and kissed her lightly on the lips. 'I'll be in my office if you need me.' He turned and walked away and she watched him, wishing desperately that she could fall in love with him. He was by far the nicest man she had ever met. He was attractive, kind, generous. Why had she been fool enough to fall for a swine like Mark Hammond when there were so many much nicer men in the world?

When she went back into the chalet Mark was in his chair again, reading the last letter. He ignored her presence as he read, his face unreadable.

Rachel poured away her cold coffee, made some fresh and sat down to drink it.

Mark laid down the letters and gave her a cool, wary look. 'There's nothing in them to give a clue. I can't believe he didn't tell you what he was up to. You may have pulled the wool over Olly's eyes, but I'm not blind, Rachel. Where is your cousin?'

'I don't know.' She spoke low and coldly, meeting his eyes.

There was a flash of fury in the blue gaze. 'Don't lie to me!'

'Ever since we met you've consistently refused to believe a word I say! I'm not going to argue with you now, just to repeat that I do not know where Derry is, nor did I have any idea what was in his mind. He would never have mentioned it to me—he knew I wouldn't approve.' Derry had hinted, of course, he had made vague threats against the Hammonds and their circle, but she had never had any glimpse of his intentions.

Mark stared at her angry face, eyes narrowed. 'Why should I believe you?'

'I don't give a damn whether you do or not.'

His face twisted savagely. 'I'm not as easy to manipulate as Nicky or Ian MacIntyre, am I?' He watched her as he spoke and saw her colour deepen at his mention of Ian.

She stood up. 'You'd better go now. There's nothing more to be said.'

'Isn't there?' He rose too, his arm catching her waist, pulling her towards him, struggling.

'Let me go!'

'Like hell,' he said thickly, staring at her mouth, and it lay between them then, that deep awareness, like a minefield prickling with danger. Rachel twisted to escape as he dragged her closer, but she was unable to take her own eyes off his lips as they descended, watching them close on her with the terrified, fascinated gaze of a rabbit as it succumbed to a stoat.

She felt as though it had been years since she was in his arms, but the second his mouth took possession the time between was wiped out and her hunger rose to swamp her common sense. He no longer needed to hold her tightly. She was lying against him weakly, her hands moving up to clasp around his neck, her head tilted back, her mouth open under his, returning his kiss passionately.

One of his hands thrust beneath the heavy weight of her rich hair, his fingers pressing against her white nape. The other slid up her back to force her body forwards against his own.

His knee forced itself between her legs, pushing her off balance. She trembled, pulling her head back. 'No, Mark.'

'Yes,' he whispered in that impeded, burning voice. She caught the brilliant, glittering flash of his eyes as he looked at her. 'Do you think you can hide it from me?'

Her lashes flickered against her cheek. 'What?'

He smiled sardonically. 'You want me as much as I want you. At least be honest about that.'

Her lids rose reluctantly and she looked into his eyes, feeling desire flood her mind and body. It was useless to try to think while he held her like this, his thighs hard against her, the aroused force of his body unhidden in this intimate embrace.

'Why should I lie?' she asked huskily, her lips trembling. 'It's the lowest common denominator, and I don't suppose it's the last time I'll ever feel like this for a man I don't like.'

His face took on a dark, flushed anger. 'You little bitch!'

'You asked for the truth!'

His hand tightened around her neck, the long fingers pressing into her flesh, hurting and exciting.

'MacIntyre doesn't make you feel like this, does he?' He sounded sharply satiric, his eyes triumphant.

She flicked him a bitter look. 'Ian is a wonderful man! I wouldn't mention the two of you in the same breath.'

Mark's mouth thinned. 'Please don't. I wouldn't like it.'

'I don't give a damn what you don't like.' Rachel

pushed at his hard chest. 'Let me go, please. I'm tired of this.'

He laughed gratingly. 'Are you?'

Suddenly she was floating, her body swept off the ground and into his arms before she knew what he meant to do. Terror caught at her. She kicked and struggled, shoving him away, but he merely grinned down at her, carrying her into the little bedroom.

He pushed her down on to the narrow white bed and held her there without difficulty, his lean body forceful, laughing as she tried to hit him, an angry mockery in his face.

After he had watched her struggles for a moment as though she was amusing him enormously, he suddenly lowered himself on top of her and forced her head round, his mouth finding hers with a violent insistence which silenced and stilled her.

She was trembling, the impact of his hard lips defeating her. The hands pushing against his shoulders tensed and lay immobile, then curled into his body, holding him with hungry possession.

She felt him slide a hand beneath her body. The swift downward glide of her zip caught her off balance and she shifted, panic-stricken. 'Please don't, Mark,' she whispered against his intruding mouth.

'Be quiet,' he muttered, his hand moving inside her dress, stroking her warm naked skin, slowly exploring the curved spine, finding the tiny mole just below her shoulder blades, following the outline of her ribs.

When he jerked the dress down from her shoulders, imprisoning her arms, she protested angrily to deaf ears. He was already tracing the frail collarbone with his lips, finding the deep hollows between the bones, brushing the whiteness above the fast-beating pulse in her throat.

The telephone broke the deep thick silence between them. Mark jumped as though he had been shot, his closed eyes opening.

'Leave it,' he muttered as she moved to get up.

'Please,' she said shakily. 'It might be the club. I work there.'

His face was stony. 'Forget it.'

'If I don't answer it, Ian will come over here to find out what I'm doing.'

Mark's face twisted cruelly. 'Then he's in for a shock.'

Her face burned. 'Please, Mark—don't!'

He looked at her as if he hated her, then moved abruptly, releasing her. Rachel fled to answer the telephone, speaking huskily into it.

'Are you all right?' Ian asked, and he sounded curt.

'Yes,' she said, knowing she sounded as disturbed and off balance as she felt. 'Do you want me there now?'

There was a silence. 'Yes, come now,' said Ian, and replaced the phone with a crash.

Mark suddenly moved behind her. She felt his fingers pulling up her zip, and their touch on her skin sent a shiver of aroused passion down her spine. Pushing a shaking hand through her ruffled hair, she said, 'I have to go over to the club.'

'So I heard,' said Mark, staring down at her as he faced her. His skin was taut over the hard bones of his face and the brilliance of his eyes told her that he was as desperately aroused as she was.

Love was a frenzy, she thought, a wildfire running

through the bloodstream, destroying as it went. She badly wanted to give in to him, to go to bed with him, knowing herself so irrevocably in love that if she never lay in his arms she would regret it to the end of her life. Did it really matter that all he felt was desire for her?

They stared at each other in a tense silence, their eyes locked in a silent battle. Mark put out his hand very slowly and touched her mouth with one finger, hunger in the movement. Charm lit his blue eyes. 'My God, you're so beautiful,' he whispered huskily.

Irony touched her face. 'So are you,' she said, her mouth curving into a smile.

His hand dropped and he smiled at her, amused, then she turned and went into the bathroom to do something about her appearance. Mark's wild love-making had left her distinctly dishevelled.

Joining him, she opened the chalet door. Mark moved reluctantly, his glance on her. 'I could wait here for you,' he said.

Her face froze. 'No, you couldn't!'

He looked angrily at her. She slammed the door and they walked to the club building without saying anything, his lean body moving gracefully at her side, their black shadows merging from time to time in the hot sunlight.

'I'll be seeing you,' he said as he halted at the double doors. 'I'm staying at the Granada.' It was the most prestigious hotel on the island, new and very modern, the furnishings and decor the height of luxury. 'Don't try to leave the island, Rachel. I would be a step behind you within an hour.'

She gave him a cold, defiant smile. 'Why should I run? You don't frighten me.'

'Then I should,' he said bitingly. His eyes were narrowed, fierce. 'I'll be back.'

Rachel walked into the club and Ian was waiting for her in the foyer. She guessed he had been watching her with Mark. His face was quiet and reflective.

She followed him into his little, air conditioned office and he gestured her to a chair, seating himself on the edge of his desk, his eyes on her.

'What's going on?' he asked crisply, and she looked at him in a dazed silence, hardly knowing how to answer him.

When she said nothing, he sighed. 'Shall I take it point by point? I rang you to ask you to do a private function the Sunday after next and you sounded as if you were scared out of your wits, then you more or less invited yourself over here without waiting to find out what I wanted.' He searched her face. 'So I ask again ... what's going on?'

'It's complicated,' Rachel said reluctantly.

'I've got all the time in the world,' Ian returned. He folded his arms and surveyed her. 'Start at the beginning and tell me all about it.'

For a moment she hesitated, but she had too many worries pressing on her mind and Ian's reliable, kindly smile was too inviting. She found herself telling him the whole story from the beginning, leaving almost nothing out. What she did leave out were the more intimate details of her meetings with Mark. She could not bring herself to tell Ian all about that.

He gave her a wry smile when she wound to an end. 'So that's why Olly sent you over to me! I might have known she was killing two birds with one stone. I wondered how you'd come to know her well enough for her to take an interest in your career.'

'She was very kind to me.'

He nodded. 'Olly can be kind, but she's also very shrewd and very decisive. Mark didn't inherit all his drive from his father, you know. There's a lot of Olly in him. The Hammonds are a ruthless family.'

Rachel's mouth compressed. He didn't know the half of it.

The brown eyes skimmed her averted face. 'Are you in love with Mark Hammond?'

The question took her by surprise. She flushed more deeply, stammering some reply. 'No! Yes. Oh, I don't know.'

Ian gave her a dry, twisted smile. 'Very revealing. And what's his angle? Or do I need to ask? I saw the way he looked at you. I've seen sharks with the same expression when they smelt blood.'

She shuddered and laughed. 'Don't!'

Ian gave her a long look. 'What do you want to do about it?'

Her brow wrinkled. 'How do you mean?'

'Do you want him driven off? Or are you going to give in?'

Her lashes swept down over her eyes, her cheeks grew scarlet. 'I'm not the sort for brief love affairs. No, I shan't give in.' She said it with a desperate ring which made Ian smile drily.

'You sound remarkably uncertain of that. There is a way of getting rid of him if you really mean that.'

She looked up, biting her lip. 'Is there?'

Ian smiled again, more kindly. 'Will you let me deal with it?'

Her face showed dismay, anxiety, doubt. 'How?'

Ian watched her. 'I would have to tell him that I had the right to protect you.'

Rachel stared, eyes opening wide. 'Oh!'

He laughed shortly. 'Don't look like that. I'm talking purely theoretically. If I go to Hammond and tell him you're going to marry me, and warn him off, he'll go, believe me. A man like Hammond doesn't invade other men's territory. If he thinks you're free, he'll try again and again until he gets what he wants. It's your choice, Rachel.'

She looked down at her shaking hands, knotting them together. 'I have no right to involve you like this.'

'Never mind that,' he said curtly. 'Is your answer for or against? Do I speak to Hammond or not?'

She couldn't look at him. 'I ... I'd be grateful if you would,' she whispered through dry lips.

There was a little silence, then Ian said quietly, 'Right. Is he coming to the club tonight?'

She nodded, still not looking at him.

'I'll see him tonight, then,' Ian said. 'Keep out of his way until then, Rachel. You can stay in the clubhouse until tonight, if you like.' He got up and moved to the door. 'And don't worry, I'll sort him out.'

She walked to the door and as she moved to open it his hand touched her arm lightly.

'There are no strings, Rachel. I'm not intending to come back with claims of my own for having seen Hammond off, don't fret about that.'

'Thank you,' she whispered, and slipped out of the office.

CHAPTER NINE

RACHEL did not see Mark again that day. She hung around the club, as Ian had suggested, helping the kitchen staff with their preparations, listening to the group rehearse a new number, talking to Benny, the cheerful club driver who had a fund of island myths which he loved to retell.

In the evening, Mark appeared at a table in the nightclub, but Rachel was careful to stay out of sight until she had to sing. She kept her eyes away from the table at which she knew he sat, her voice faintly unsteady once or twice from nerves. A brief glance towards him as she acknowledged the applause when she had finished showed her that Ian was at his table, his face calm, and that Mark's features were dark and hard, his mouth tautly unsmiling.

Ian had told him. She backed, smiling artificially, and vainly tried to stop herself shaking.

Ian walked back with her to her chalet, holding her arm, aware, she suspected, that she was shaking.

'What did he say?' she asked in dry tones.

'Very little.' Ian looked sideways at her, his eyes compassionate. 'You've got it badly, haven't you, Rachel? I didn't realise how badly until now.' He squeezed her arm. 'I think he'll fly back to London tomorrow. Don't worry.'

Alone in the chalet she lay in bed listening to the warm, breathing darkness outside, and her heart ached. Visions of Mark flashed across her mind: his contemptuous face on that first evening, his passion whenever he had kissed her, his ruthless pursuit of her ever since they met, the charm of which she had unwillingly become aware. She ought to hate and despise him. It galled her to accept that she loved him. He was a man to whom love was an unknown factor. She was just wasting her time in loving him, but she was helpless to change her feelings.

Restless, she got up early next morning and went down to the beach as usual. It was empty and she had the blue water to herself until her attention was drawn to another figure stalking down the sands and wading into the waves. Her heart thudded. Mark!

He swam strongly towards her. She had a momentary impulse to flee, then sanity commanded her to behave calmly as though nothing odd was happening inside her. She gave him a cool, offhand greeting.

'You're up early.'

He floated, his black hair trailing on the water. 'I wanted to talk to you.'

Her face betrayed her nervousness and he grimaced.

'Don't worry, I'm not going to make another grab at you. I've had news from England. Little Julia Brennan is back with her father.'

Relief brought a sigh and smile from her. 'Oh, I'm glad! Is she all right?' She searched his blue eyes. 'Derry didn't harm her?'

His mouth twisted, cynicism in his face. 'I'm beginning to wonder who was chasing who! Apparently sweet little Julia spent a blissful few days with your cousin and then dumped him.' His eyes had a sardonic gleam. 'I almost feel sorry for him. I spoke to Julia.

She giggled a lot and gave me to understand she'd had Derry on a string until she was tired of him, then she walked out.'

Rachel's skin went cold. Poor Derry! Her throat closed and she said sharply, 'So she was not a threatened innocent at all!'

Mark watched her angry face. 'It seems not. Her father was breathing smoke and fire, but Julia has always twisted him round her little finger. I doubt if she'll suffer any real punishment.'

'Of course not,' Rachel said flatly. 'It's Derry who's been made a fool of, in the end.' She thought of Derry's plans to hit back at the arrogant, moneyed world which the Hammonds inhabited, and felt angry and compassionate at the same time. Poor Derry! What must he be feeling at the moment?

Mark gave her a wry smile. 'His motives were hardly praiseworthy. Do you expect me to believe he was in love with the girl?'

She flushed. 'I doubt it, and it's just as well, isn't it? If he had been, he'd be feeling pretty sick now.' She turned and swam back towards the beach, aware that Mark was close behind her. As she waded out of the water, her hair streaming with salt wetness, her golden skin damply gleaming, he appeared at her side.

'I gather congratulations are in order.' His voice was coolly calm.

'Thank you.' She picked up the beach towel lying on the sand beside the book and sunglasses she had brought down with her. Mark stood watching as she dried her body roughly.

'I thought you were waiting for true love,' he said in a sharp, sardonic voice.

Her skin coloured and she gave him a quick, angry look. 'When are you flying back to England?'

He smiled at that. 'Is that a hint that I'm to ask no questions?'

'It's none of your business.'

'You don't even pretend you love him.' The flat delivery held accusation and her eyes shifted restlessly under his stare. 'How could you even pretend it with me? I know only too well that you don't, Rachel. You made it very obvious yesterday.'

She took a deep breath, facing him, her slender body tense. 'I'm very fond of Ian. I respect and like him.'

Mark watched her intently. 'But it's me you want to go to bed with.' The quiet statement made her face flame.

She bit her lip, disturbed and shaken. 'I told you yesterday, that doesn't mean a thing. Physical attraction is something over which one has no control.'

His dark brows arched. 'And love is?'

'No, of course not.' She felt like hitting him, but she made herself stay calm. 'That may come in time if it has enough of a groundwork, and my feelings for Ian provide that groundwork.'

'So you're choosing to settle for what you can get rather than what you want?' He sounded reflective, as though her motives interested him in a theoretical sense, his own emotions totally uninvolved.

She shrugged. 'This isn't a discussion I want. Good-bye, Mark.' She picked up her book and sunglasses and walked away, leaving him on the empty golden sands.

She expected to hear that he had flown off back to

England, but he was in the club that evening, sitting alone at a table, his dark face lit by the flickering candle held by a glass rose which stood beside his drink. Ian brought her into the club a quarter of an hour later to dance with him and as they moved around the floor she was conscious of Mark's unmoving stare.

'Have you seen him today?' Ian asked her, and she gave him a brittle smile.

'Yes, this morning.'

'Was he behaving himself?' Ian's frown darkened his face. 'Or do you want me to throw him out of the club?'

She laughed. 'Could you? It would be difficult, wouldn't it, as his mother is a large shareholder?'

Ian gave her a faint grin. 'Difficult but not impossible.'

'Do you think he would go?' She could not help sounding wry.

Ian shrugged. 'I might have to use force.'

'And you might live to regret it.' She was unable to take the idea seriously. 'I wouldn't want you to offend Mark Hammond on my account.' She gave him a warm look, her eyes affectionate. 'And he isn't causing any trouble, actually.'

Mark did not come near her, indeed. She danced with Ian for a while, then he walked her back to her chalet and paused at the door, looking down at her with a questioning look. Sensing that he wanted to kiss her, she turned up her face and his mouth lightly brushed over her lips. 'Goodnight, Rachel,' he said a little unsteadily, walking away.

The trees rustled in the distance, the moon swam

like a melancholy white face through the velvet darkness of the sky. Strange shadows leapt and twisted
around her as she opened her door and went into the
chalet.

Mark was on the beach next morning as she walked
down the sands. Their eyes met and her face betrayed
her dismay. She gave him a quick, nervous look, taking
in the lithe, hard body from head to toe, wishing the
sight of it did not quicken her pulses. He looked fit
and powerful in the brief black swimming gear and
she saw he had been diving. He noted her curious
glance at the equipment and smiled. 'We must go
down together some time. How expert are you by
now?'

'Still a beginner,' she admitted. 'What about you?'

He shrugged the broad brown shoulders. 'I've been
diving for years.' He watched her drop her towel and
the other things she was carrying. She ran down the
beach into the water and Mark was close behind her.
They swam for an hour, only speaking occasionally,
the glitter of the blue water, the shimmer of the sun
giving the morning a beauty which she found heart-
breaking.

'Where are you going now?' he asked as she gath-
ered her things together later.

'Rehearsal.'

'Have lunch with me?' The question was put quietly
and she looked at him, biting her lower lip.

'I don't think that would be a good idea.'

His smile was faint, the strong mouth only just moving. 'Please, Rachel.'

Her heart flipped. She looked quickly, incredulously, at him and saw his face serious as she met his

eyes. Common sense dictated that she refuse, but she heard herself saying weakly, 'Well, I . . .'

'I'll pick you up at twelve-thirty,' he said before she could finish the sentence, then he moved away rapidly.

Rachel went through her rehearsal without being truly aware of what she was singing, her face absorbed in her inner thoughts. Ian walked in just before the end and she flushed as she saw him.

She felt ludicrously guilty, despite the fact that their 'engagement' was a fraud. Ian had spoken to Mark to help her and she was behaving like a fool when she allowed Mark to see her. If Ian knew of it he would quite rightly regard her with amazement and scorn.

'Your voice is in good shape,' he told her as he walked with her to the club entrance.

Flushed, she said, 'Thank you. Ian, there's something I want to tell you. I'm . . .' Her words broke off as Ian lifted his head and stared at Mark's lounging figure in the foyer. He moved towards them and Ian looked down at Rachel, his brows drawn together, question in his eyes.

'Ready?' Mark asked her quietly.

She looked at Ian unhappily, her eyes filled with apology. He turned on his heel without a word and walked away. Rachel stared after him and felt sick.

Mark watched her face for a moment, then his hand touched her lightly on the arm. She jumped as though she had been shot and looked at him.

'The car's outside.' He sounded guarded, his eyes watchful.

During the drive into the town she said nothing, staring at the tropical gardens they passed, the thick waxen green leaves shadowy. Mark looked at her from time to time but said nothing. Arriving at his hotel he guided her into the bar and ordered drinks. The waiter brought them large menu cards and while they drank they studied them before giving their order. After that they sat in silence, staring at their drinks while around them other guests talked and laughed.

The waiter came to tell them that their first course was ready and they walked through into the large, sunlit dining-room to take their places at the table. Mark had ordered a dry white wine with their seafood cocktail, and it released the tension as it entered Rachel's bloodstream. Mark began to talk about Nicky, his tone light, and she found herself laughing as he described the running battle between Nicky and Jane Palfrey.

'When Nicky has finished his studies I plan to take him into the firm in the States, but in time I hope he'll take over the British end of the business.'

'By the sound of it he'll miss Jane,' Rachel commented, watching him over her glass.

He grinned at her. 'I hope so.'

She made a little face. 'Unashamed matchmaking?'

Mark's thick dark lashes flickered, a smile on his mouth. 'I'm leaving it strictly to them, but surely even you would allow me to have hopes for the future?'

She smiled then, her face relaxing. 'Of course, and from what I saw of them together you might get your wish. Jane's a nice girl and I know she likes Nicky a lot.'

'There's no hurry,' said Mark. 'He's only just eighteen.' A red wine had arrived with their steak and he watched her lifting her glass, her cheeks slightly flushed by now. 'Go easy with that. You haven't much of a head for wine.'

She laughed, her eyes involuntarily provocative and

defiant. 'How would you know?' The wine was sparkling in her blood and she felt light and happy, aware of
the sunlight around them, the blue gleam of his eyes
and the smile on his hard mouth.

She told him some of her earlier life, going into
humorous detail as she retold old anecdotes of sordid
lodging houses, sour landladies and grasping theatrical
managers up and down the country. 'Derry could
charm the birds off a tree. He always got us the best
rooms, the best terms. I don't know what I would have
done without him.'

Mark glanced down the warm curve of her slender
body, his eyes wry. 'I image you would have survived,
at least as far as the men were concerned.'

Rachel made a face. 'Oh, I had trouble with some.
of them, but Derry was very useful in pushing them
off with a boathook.'

'You're not hard enough for that sort of world,'
Mark said quietly. 'It ought to have toughened you,
but it doesn't seem to have done so.'

Rachel laughed. 'I'm tough enough, don't worry.'

He smiled drily. 'Are you?'

She looked into the blue eyes and her heart plunged
helplessly. She looked away, swallowing, suddenly
aware that she was trembling.

She refused a sweet and joined Mark in coffee, the
large silver pot left on the table with an electric hot-
plate keeping it at the right temperature. Mark said
with a grin, 'You need this! It may sober you up. I
don't want MacIntyre coming after me with a hatchet.'

They lingered over coffee, their talk by now easy
and intimate. Mark talked about a biography he had
just read and she discovered that he had a passion for

the nineteenth century, particularly the lives of politicians. 'It reveals so much about human nature that hasn't changed despite our modern gadgetry and welfare states,' he said wryly.

'I doubt if human nature ever changes,' she said. 'I expect people were just the same in the days of the Pharaohs.'

He nodded, his eyes keen. 'In my world a knowledge of human nature is essential. People who don't need to make a study of it are lucky. It can be a disillusioning experience.'

She frowned. 'You're too cynical.'

Strangely he looked regretful. 'I expect you're right. If I am, I've been pushed into it. A tree grows the way of the prevailing wind.'

She looked down into her coffee. 'You're a man, not a tree.'

He laughed softly. 'So I am,' he murmured under his breath.

'We all have a choice about our way of looking at the world,' Rachel said earnestly. 'Of course there are things which are wrong in every part of the world. People can be cruel, hard, grasping. There's disease, misery, death in some countries, rotten systems, corruption, self-seeking. But there are other things which are very much right. People can be kind, thoughtful and unselfish. Corruption can be fought. Systems can be changed. We don't just have to sit down and say: that's that. We can go out and change the world we live in, if we really don't like it.'

Mark watched her without a flicker of expression. 'And then there's love,' he said at last with a hard intonation. 'You didn't mention that, Rachel.'

She looked at him unguardedly. 'There's always love,' she agreed. 'In every corner of the world. All sorts of love—the love of a mother for a child, of a child for a mother, of ...' She broke off, her face very flushed, her eyes restless.

'Of a woman for a man,' Mark finished for her levelly.

She stood up clumsily. 'I should be getting back. It's getting late.'

They said nothing as they drove back to the club. The car had a sunroof. The wind blew through her hair, whipping it backwards in a trail of soft tendrils. The wine still flushed her cheeks and her eyes had a brilliance which drew Mark's occasional glance.

He dropped her, bidding her a quiet farewell, and she walked to her chalet, feeling uneasily that the time she had spent with him had only intensified her feeling for him and that he knew it. His last remark had hinted at it.

Ian dropped in at the chalet just before sunset. Rachel met his gaze uneasily. He talked about the private function at which she was to sing later on and when he had stopped speaking there was a difficult silence.

'Are you angry with me, Ian?' she asked tentatively.

He met her eyes directly. 'Do you think I should be?'

Her flush deepened. 'I'm behaving irrationally, I know that. I should have refused to have lunch with him, but ...'

'But you couldn't,' he said flatly, his mouth compressing. 'You don't have to explain to me, Rachel, but I think you owe an explanation to yourself. I went out of my way to give Hammond the impression we were in love and he must be laughing himself sick this afternoon.'

Her cheeks flamed. 'No!' Ian stared at her and she went on quietly, 'I don't think so, Ian. He—he more or less knows how things are.'

Ian pushed a hand through his hair. 'Meaning what?'

She spread helpless hands. 'It was kind of you, but I think it's too late to pull the wool over his eyes. I've given myself away to him.'

Ian looked pityingly at her. 'My dear girl, you only had to keep him at a distance. He would have gone. Of course he's still hanging around with you encouraging him the way you are.'

She walked to the window and stared out at the bright, artificial beauty of the club grounds. 'I love him.'

There was a silence, then Ian walked to the door and went out without another word.

Mark did not appear that evening, and the sick disappointment Rachel felt was warning enough for her. He was rapidly becoming a necessity for her and she took the dull sensation of misery to bed with her, huddling under the thin sheet with a desire to die which alarmed her.

When she saw him on the sand next morning her spirits flew upward like an imprisoned bird let loose and she could not help the brilliance of the smile she gave him.

They swam and then lay on the beach in the morning sunshine, talking. It was a curiously impersonal conversation. Mark ranged from politics to business, his head propped on his folded arms, his eyes fixed on the sweeping blue sky overhead. A few birds wheeled whitely over the incoming tide. From the club grounds came the rustle of the trees and the sound of voices as other sunbathers appeared.

Mark sat up, his lean body vigorous, dusting sand off his shoulders and arms. 'How about some coffee or are you rehearsing today?'

Rachel shook her head. 'No, no rehearsal.' They walked back to her chalet and she made coffee while Mark looked through her little store of paperback books, grinning over some of the titles.

'When are you going back to the States?' she asked, partly because she needed to know and partly because it was something to ask.

He sat down, leaning his black head against the cushion of the chair. The blue eyes watched her thoughtfully. 'Eager to see the back of me?'

She flushed, placing the coffee on the low table. 'I just wondered, that's all.'

'I've no plans,' he said.

She stared at her coffee. No plans? she asked herself. Or had he?

'Exactly what is going on between you and Mac-Intyre?' Mark asked in a level voice.

Rachel smiled bitterly. 'Nothing,' she said. 'Not a thing, and you know it.'

Mark nodded. 'You asked him to speak to me?'

'Yes.'

He looked sharply at her. 'How much did you tell him?'

'Everything,' Rachel said as if accusing him.

He drew in his lower lip. 'I don't like that.'

'I'm sorry.' The apology was insincere, brusque.

'You had no business to tell him anything. I don't want MacIntyre knowing so much about me.'

She was suddenly burningly angry. 'Then get out of our lives. Take a plane, take a boat—swim. But go away, Mark, for God's sake!'

Leaving his coffee untouched, he stood up, pushing back the chair as he moved. 'You sound as if you mean that.'

'Every word.' Rachel looked up at him bitterly. 'Every damned word.'

He went so quietly that for a moment she thought she was imagining it, but when she looked around again the room was empty and the silence mocked her.

Over the next few days her mood was grim and Ian looked at her with irritated compassion as he spoke to her. 'He flew to England two days ago,' he told her. 'I checked at his hotel.'

She nodded. 'Well, that's that.' She smiled with difficulty. 'Thank you for what you did, Ian. I really appreciate it.'

'I didn't do a thing but make a fool of myself,' said Ian. 'If I'd realised just how deeply you were involved with him I would never have spoken to him.'

Her face had a weary pallor. 'I'm sorry. It's my fault.'

'Yes,' Ian said almost harshly, 'it is.' Then he looked at her with a resigned smile. 'But forget it. No harm done. He really has gone this time.' A silence, then he asked flatly, 'Did he get what he came for?'

Rachel felt heat flooding into her veins. 'No, he did not!'

Ian grimaced. 'I'm sorry—I just wondered. Forget I asked.'

The halcyon somnolence of the island closed in on

her again and she found her days becoming confined to her hours in the sea and her work at the club. She refused all invitations to lunch or dine with Ian and in time he stopped asking, accepting that there was no future in their relationship. Rachel had had enough of commitments. Ian was a nice man and she liked him, but she wanted nothing to do with any man.

As her contract drew to a close she was able to contemplate a return to London with relief. She had saved a large sum from her high salary. Even if she took some time to get another job, she would be free from financial worries for a time, and she was feeling homesick for the grey London streets she knew she would find when she flew home.

She had not heard a word from Derry for months. She had written to him without reply. She suspected that he had been humiliated by Julia Brennan. It was unlikely that he had been in love with the girl, but his self-esteem would have taken quite a knock when he realised she was using him as ruthlessly as he would have used her. Rachel hoped that it would have taught Derry a lesson, but she doubted it. Under her cousin's charming smile lay too much hardness for him to benefit from such an experience. Derry was as cynical about love as Mark Hammond. They neither of them believed in its existence.

Saying goodbye to Ian proved harder than she had anticipated. He drove her to the airport in a withdrawn mood which puzzled her. At the gate through which she had to pass to board he pulled her close and kissed her with a hard searching which disturbed and worried her, then walked away without a backward look. She got on her plane realising with a sensation of guilt that she had somehow made a dent in Ian's heart. She blamed herself for never having noticed it. She had known he liked her, even that he found her attractive, but that there might be more to his feelings than that had never occurred to her.

He was too kind and likeable for her to forget the pain she must have caused him. Her soft heart was wrung. She sat in her seat all the way to London brooding over the harm she might have caused without realising it.

It was not the first time that she had discovered that a man was in love with her, but Ian was the first whom she had ever sensed she could have loved in return. If she had never met Mark Hammond she might have learnt to care for Ian. It was tragic, she thought, staring at the drifting white clouds below the wings of the plane. What a waste of opportunity! In other circumstances, at another time, she might have become Ian's wife and lived very happily for the rest of her life.

Arriving at London, she went straight to a hotel in a quiet back street of Islington. She had given up her London flat before she went to the Bahamas and would have to find somewhere else. It was raining, a thin drizzle which she felt with something akin to delight since it meant she was back home. She felt no regret as yet for the blue skies and sunshine of the Bahamas.

That evening she rang Derry and discovered for the first time that he had left his London flat and had not given the landlord a forwarding address.

Alarmed, she rang his parents and discovered that he was not even in England. He had, they told her, gone to Germany to work and would not be back for

some time. He had been gone for just over a week,
which was why they had not mentioned it before.
'Didn't he tell you?' they asked in some surprise, since
he and Rachel had always been so close. She put the
phone down with a sad smile. Her old close relationship with Derry had long been over, but it was only
now that she realised how far apart they had drifted.

That winter was the longest and coldest of her life. She
trudged from agency to agency in search of work, but
it was not until she met a bright-eyed brunette called
Karen Spark that she finally found a job. They met in
a waiting-room and fell into talk. Karen mentioned a
pantomime which was opening in Brighton after
Christmas and suggested they both audition.

'I've never done anything like that,' Rachel protested.

Karen eyed her, smiling. 'There's always a first time.
Oh, come on, pantos are fun. The kids love them and
there's a great atmosphere backstage.'

Rachel considered it, then grimaced. 'Well, why
not?'

'With your legs you should walk into a job,' Karen
laughed. 'Mine are like piano legs, unfortunately!'

Nevertheless Karen's engaging personality and
bright eyes got her a job in the chorus when they audi-
tioned. Rachel, to her surprise, was heard twice and
then given a small part. She had never done any acting
before, but in rehearsals she soon discovered she enjoyed it.

'You're a natural,' Karen encouraged her. The two
girls moved into a flat together, sharing food and
household tasks, their friendship growing as they got

to know each other. Rachel suppressed all mention of Mark and even skirted the subject of her months in the Bahamas, although it had been mention of those which had, she suspected, got her the job in the panto.

Karen was a lively, cheerful girl, prone to fall in love at the drop of a hat, and out again within days. Her boy-friends tended to be large, burly young men with little conversation who gazed at her with awe.

She had a married sister living two miles from them and would willingly babysit for her at short notice, which did not please her young men. It cramped their style to have a two-year-old eavesdropping whenever they tried to cuddle Karen.

Bobby was a sturdy child with curly blond hair and big blue eyes. Everywhere he went he carried his teddy-bear, a large pink object with black eyes which Karen had given him when he was a baby. Tattered and motheaten by now, it bore the marks of love on every inch of it, ears chewed, nose battered, fur worn down through over-affectionate cuddles.

'I want Ludo,' Bobby would chant as Karen settled him for a nap, and she would thrust the bear into his arms with a fond beam. 'One day that bear will disintegrate,' she would inform him, and Bobby would stare, round-eyed and baffled, sucking Ludo's ear thoughtfully.

A week before Christmas Karen was out shopping when her sister arrived, lugging Bobby under one arm, her face flushed. 'Oh, glory,' she groaned, 'I've got to go to the hospital this morning.' She gave Rachel a sheepish grin. 'I think I'm pregnant again, in fact I'm sure of it, and I didn't want to take Bobby there. He will run about and shout, and the nurses get so ratty.'

'I'll look after him,' Rachel offered, smiling at Bobby. 'He's no trouble. He can help me get the lunch.'

When his mother had gone Bobby was very happy following Rachel around the tiny flat, Ludo in one hand, watching her do her work. When the door bell went again Rachel said to him cheerfully, 'There's Auntie Karen, I expect! Come and kiss her, Bobby.'

Opening the door with a smile she stopped short, her face changing as she saw Mark on the doorstep.

She could find nothing to say to him, her colour ebbing away. Bobby tugged at her skirt, whispering, 'Who's that, Auntie?'

She bent and lifted him into her arms as if he were a shield, facing Mark nervously. He glanced at the boy and then back at her. 'May I come in?'

Rachel hesitated, but could find no excuse for refusing, so stepped back in silence and let him walk past her into the flat. Mark stood there, formally elegant in a heavy black overcoat, his sleek dark head lifted as he looked around the untidy room. Bobby had left a comic on the floor. There were Karen's ballet slippers flung down, laces trailing, a coffee cup and a little pile of records on a table. The flat was furnished in an old-fashioned style, cosy but distinctly out of date.

'Want a drink,' Bobby chatted, beaming.

Mark turned a slight smile towards her. 'May I join him?'

She gave him a harassed, puzzled look. 'Of course. Coffee?'

'Orange juice,' Bobby reproved, patting her cheek.

Absently she kissed his dimpled baby hand. 'I know,

darling.' She glanced at Mark, her eyes questioning.

'Coffee, please,' he said promptly.

She went into the little kitchen, dropped Bobby on a chair and put on the coffee before making his orange juice and handing it to his eager fingers. Mark undid his coat, watching her and she glimpsed the smooth dark suit he wore, the whiteness of his shirt immaculate. Rachel moved around making the coffee, thinking desperately. What was he doing here?

Having finished his orange juice Bobby wandered off to watch the small television. They heard the sound roar as he turned it up and Rachel hurriedly went through and turned it down before one of the neighbours complained. Bobby lay on his stomach, feet kicking in the air, watching solemnly as a lady in a blue overall did flower arrangements and talked in a breathless voice.

Going back into the kitchen she was surprised to see Mark smoking. He caught her quick glance and grimaced. 'I know. I kicked the habit once, but it's caught up with me again.'

'You shouldn't,' she said, pouring his coffee. With her back to him she asked anxiously, 'Why are you here, Mark?'

He was silent and she turned to look at him. He had his back to her and was stubbing out his cigarette, his neck faintly red. Slowly he turned and she saw an almost haggard look in his face, his bones sharp under the taut pale skin.

'I love you,' he said huskily.

Rachel's hand shook. She put down the cup of coffee she was holding out to him, feeling her body tremble violently.

He hadn't moved. He was standing there staring at her intensely, his blue eyes filled with a vulnerability she had never thought to see in them.

'Don't,' she muttered, swinging away. Was this the latest turn of the screw? His latest attempt to get her to admit him to her bed?

'I'm not going to touch you,' Mark said harshly. 'I've been fighting this for months and I've gone past thinking that it would alter anything for me to put my arms round you. You're inside my head, in my bloodstream, under my skin. If I never saw you again I wouldn't stop loving you.'

She listened, her back to him, her whole attention given to what he was saying, forced to believe he meant it by the driven note in his voice. She had never heard Mark speak so seriously.

'It started for me the night we met,' he went on. 'I didn't know what had hit me, only that each time I saw you I found myself getting more and more involved with you.'

She turned slowly, looking at him with searching incredulity.

He looked at her, then away, his hands clenched at his sides as though he were on the point of violence. 'I was even jealous of Nicky! A boy of that age, my own son, and I couldn't stand watching you smile at him.' His mouth twisted in self-mockery. 'Before I met you I had a distinct picture of you, the sort of woman who accepted diamond bracelets from a seventeen-year-old, a nightclub singer who could make trouble for the family.'

Rachel smiled bitterly. 'I know what you thought of me. You were very explicit on the point.'

His black head came up with a jerk. 'Within twenty-four hours I had to force myself to believe it could be true, Rachel! Hell, I was too confused to know what to think by then. You had me going round in circles until I was dizzy.' The blue eyes blazed. 'I couldn't believe you were on the level—it didn't seem possible. I tried everything I knew to undermine you. When I wrote you that cheque my hand was shaking. God! If you knew how I felt when you tore it up.'

'You looked furious,' she said wryly.

'Because you said the price had doubled,' Mark muttered. 'There were too many emotions running round my head. I just didn't know what to make of you. You threw my book of rules out of the window.'

She laughed at that, her eyes dancing. 'It was a silly book, anyway.'

He took a step forward, his eyes on her warm mouth, and the smile withered under the passionate look he gave her.

'I knew from the start that you attracted me. In other circumstances I'd have gone all out to get you, but that business with Nicky confused me.'

'That's not how I remember it,' Rachel commented drily.

He gave her a brief, amused look. 'I made a few exploratory passes,' he admitted. 'But I didn't push it too far because I wasn't sure what you were up to.'

'I wasn't up to anything,' she said flatly. 'Nicky was a nice boy and I was sorry for him. I didn't want to hurt him and it seemed to me that the easiest way to deal with the crush he had on me was to play it down as hard as I could. I knew he'd soon get over it.'

Mark watched her face intently. 'I believe that now.

I had to get to know you to believe it, though, Rachel.
I just wasn't used to meeting young women with
honest motives and no axe to grind.'

'There's a first time for everything!' Her tone was
flippant, her face guarded. She moved to the door.
'Well, I'm glad you understand me now. I've got a lot
to do this morning, Mark. I'll see you out.'

He stood there as though he couldn't believe what
he was hearing, his face darkening.

'Have you forgotten that I said I loved you?'

She held on to the door-frame tightly, giving him a
polite smile. 'No, I haven't forgotten, and I'm flattered . . .'

'Flattered!' The word shot out of him like a bullet
from a gun, his blue eyes flaring in violence.

Gently she said, 'In some ways you're like Nicky.'
The comparison made his face tighten and grow hard,
but she went on, 'You're both used to a world where
the standards are false. I've no doubt that when you
realised I had no ulterior motives you found it impressive, Mark, but you don't love me. You just think
you do. In a few months you won't even remember my
name.'

He pushed his hands into his pockets. 'I won't?'

Aware of the menacing glitter in the blue eyes, she
lifted her chin proudly and said, 'No.'

A key turned in the front door and they both
jumped at the sound. Karen came in, whipping a head-
scarf off her head. 'Hi, I'm back!' Her mouth opened
as she caught sight of Mark, her eyes rounding. She
looked at Rachel, a dazed question in her face.

Rachel huskily introduced her and Mark held out
his strong, well-shaped hand, a faint smile on his

mouth as Karen gazed at him in unhidden admiration. She had never seen anyone like him and her face innocently confessed as much, travelling over the lithe figure, the expensive formal clothes, the gloss of luxury which covered him from head to foot.

Bobby darted out and caught Karen's leg, hugging her. 'Auntie, did you bring me some sweeties?'

'Hallo, pest,' Karen smiled at him. 'What are you doing here?'

'Mummy went to the hospital,' he explained cheerfully.

Mark gave Karen one of his most charming smiles. 'Now that you are back it leaves Rachel free to come and see my mother, doesn't it?' He gave Rachel a demanding glance. 'Olly wants to see you very much.'

She was flushed and uneasy, her tone stammering. 'I'm sorry, I have too much to do today.'

'Go on, Ray,' Karen urged, not understanding her reluctance. She looked Rachel over. 'I should change first, though. You're dressed for housework, not visiting.'

Mark gave Rachel a slight push. 'Please,' he said, not bothering to hide from Karen his urgency.

Reluctantly she went and changed, putting on a green dress which clung tightly to her until it reached her hips where it flared into a fullness which rustled as she walked. Over it she wore a dark brown fur-collared coat tied at the waist.

Mark's glance summed her up briefly, a glitter in his eyes, then he made a smiling remark to Karen and ushered Rachel out of the flat. She gave him an irritated look.

He did not drive to his mother's house. Turning the

car north, he drove out to Hampstead Heath where he parked and persuaded Rachel to walk over the dry, rustling grass with him. 'We have to talk,' he said, his hand clamped restrainingly on her arm.

'There's nothing to talk about.' Rachel's face was mutinous, her eyes wary.

'You're damned right,' he muttered under his breath. Pushing her into the lee of a large hollybush, he took her into his arms, looking down into her flushed, angry face. 'The time for talking has stopped,' he said, before he began to kiss her hungrily.

It had always been the same, she thought, as she quickened with desire under the hard mouth. Whatever insults they had flung at each other, whatever the basic antagonism which had risen between them since their first meeting, he only had to touch her for a consuming fire to run along her veins.

He pushed his hands into her hair, thrusting back her head, bringing his mouth down fiercely as if he could not have enough of the feel of her lips under his own. 'Oh, God, I love you,' he muttered, kissing her.

When he finally lifted his mouth she was almost fainting, yet she managed to open her eyes to look at him with a bitterness she could not hide. 'All right, Mark,' she sighed. 'I haven't got the courage to run any more. I'm going to hate myself in the future, but just now I can't see any option.' Her lashes flickered, wetness on them. 'I'll accept your terms.'

Mark's hard face was like something carved in stone. His blue eyes had narrowed on her face, their expression unreadable. She had expected passion, triumph and there was nothing in his face at all.

'Is that an unreserved submission?' he asked with a faint dryness in his tone.

Her mouth quivered as though he had hit her. 'Yes, damn you,' she muttered.

'Why?' he asked shortly, and she stared at him, bewildered.

'You know why—what do you mean, why?'

'Are you admitting you love me?'

The question had the incisive clarity of a knife and she reacted with anger. 'Yes, I love you—and I wish to God I didn't!'

'Don't, my darling,' he said in a deep, moved voice. His arms encircled her again, one hand stroking her hair. 'Did you think I was asking you to be my mistress again? Rachel, I love you. I want you for my wife.'

Trembling, she leaned against him, her mouth dry. 'Mark—oh, Mark, I can't marry you.'

He stood still. 'What do you mean, you can't?' He pushed her head up and looked deep into her eyes. His face was pale. 'Why not?'

'We're from different worlds. You said it yourself. I could never be the sort of wife you need. It wouldn't work.'

His face relaxed. A smile lit his eyes. 'Hell, my darling, I'd make it work. If there are problems we'll work at them together.' He touched her cheek, his hand gentle. 'I'm not a young man, Rachel. I've found the impossible dream late in life and I wouldn't want to go on living without it. Do you think I hadn't thought it all out? Why do you think I left you in the Bahamas, stayed away for months? I had to be certain that the way I felt for you was real. I took a risk, leaving you with MacIntyre. If you knew me you would know what a gamble I took.'

She frowned. 'I don't understand.'

Mark's mouth was crooked. 'He seemed to be all the

things you were looking for—a decent, reliable hus-band. I hated his guts.' The blue eyes were savage. 'I was so jealous of him I could have shoved a knife into him. But he'd made it clear he loved you and wanted to marry you, and I had to admit he'd make a better husband for you than I would. I knew you found me attractive—you couldn't hide that from me, darling. I wasn't sure I had the right to take advantage of my physical effect on you. I wanted you to be free to choose. So I went.'

Dazed, she stared at him. 'You thought I might marry Ian?'

'I was terrified you would,' he nodded grimly.

'Yet you went away?'

'Rachel, I'm no angel,' Mark muttered. 'I've led a pretty hectic life. I'm not good enough for you. But I'll make you happy if it kills me. I love you more than I've ever loved anyone or anything in my life.'

She gave him a disbelieving, quivering smile. 'Are you saying that for once in your life you did something against your own interest?'

His colour deepened, his mouth quirked. 'Crazy as it seems, yes.'

'How altruistic of you, Mr Hammond,' she smiled, looking at him through her lashes. 'Or were you hop-ing I would marry him and let you off the hook?'

His face darkened. 'Hoping it! I was scared stiff of it.' He took her face in his hands. 'But you didn't marry him. When I discovered you'd come back to London I knew I had a chance with you.'

'I think you had as many doubts as I do,' she said soberly. 'We just aren't right for each other.'

He kissed her fiercely, hurting, his mouth an unsatiated demand which left her soft mouth bruised and aching. 'We love each other. That leaves no room for doubts.'

She wriggled out of his arms and walked back to his car, saying over her shoulder, 'I can't marry you.'

Mark caught up with her, kissed her with the same savagery. 'You will,' he told her deeply. 'Now come and tell Olly with me.'

She walked with him, but she said again, 'I can't. I won't.'

'You will,' he said as they reached the car.

'Mark, listen to me,' Rachel groaned.

'Kiss me,' he said in retort, smiling with a wicked amusement which sent her heart spinning like a top.

She held him off, doubt and yearning in her face. 'Darling, I can't marry you.'

'You will,' he said with that firm assurance.

And she did.

Titles available this month in the
Mills & Boon ROMANCE Series

CHATEAU IN THE PALMS *by Anne Hampson*
Philippe de Chameral could have made Jane happy — but
he did not know that she was a married woman . . .

SAVAGE POSSESSION *by Margaret Pargeter*
Melissa had been too used to having her own way to allow
Ryan Trevelyan to dominate her — but she soon had to
change her tune!

ONE MORE RIVER TO CROSS *by Essie Summers*
Rebecca was as different from her flighty cousin Becky as
chalk from cheese, but the girls' identical appearance was to
get Rebecca into a difficult situation with the bossy Darroch . . .

LURE OF EAGLES *by Anne Mather*
An unknown cousin had inherited the family business, and
Domine found herself agreeing to the masterful Luis Aguilar's
suggestion that she accompany him to South America to meet
the girl.

MIDNIGHT SUN'S MAGIC *by Betty Neels*
Could Annis ever make Jake see that she had married him for
love, and not on the rebound?

LOVE IS A FRENZY *by Charlotte Lamb*
Seventeen-year-old Nicky Hammond's devotion was touching,
but Rachel couldn't possibly return it. Yet how could she
convince his disapproving father Mark that she wasn't cradle-
snatching — or worse?

THIS SIDE OF PARADISE *by Kay Thorpe*
Gina's so-called friend was after a man with money, so Gina
couldn't really blame Ryan Barras when he got entirely the
wrong idea about her . . .

A LAND CALLED DESERET *by Janet Dailey*
LaRaine had always been able to twist men round her finger
but, as luck would have it, she fell in love with Travis
McCrea — who had no time for her at all!

TANGLED SHADOWS *by Flora Kidd*
Kathryn could hardly refuse to return to her husband when
she learned from his family that he had lost his memory in
an accident — but would he remember what had destroyed
the marriage in the first place?

THE PASSIONATE WINTER *by Carole Mortimer*
Piers Sinclair was her boy-friend's father: older, more
sophisticated, far more experienced than she was. And so of
course Leigh fell in love with him . . .

— all that's pleasurable in Romantic Reading!
Available October 1979

Forthcoming Mills & Boon Romances

THE KURRANULLA ROUND *by Dorothy Cork*
Matty's uncle wanted to see her married to Dirk Reasoner,
but Matty knew something her uncle didn't — and that was
why Dirk would never trust and respect her, let alone love
her . . .

ACROSS THE GREAT DIVIDE *by Kerry Allyne*
It was Jerome whom Nicole loved — so why was it the annoy-
ing Lang Jamieson who occupied so much of her thoughts?

FLAME OF DIABLO *by Sara Craven*
Vitas de Mendoza agreed to help Rachel find her brother —
but at a price. Would she find the price too high? Or would
she pay — far too willingly?

BLUE LOTUS *by Margaret Way*
Susan was rescued from the rain forest of Queensland by
Devin Chandler and taken to recover at his cattle station — a
private kingdom where the king made his own laws . . .

FRUSTRATION *by Charlotte Lamb*
Considering the tumultuous circumstances of their first
meeting, it was hardly surprising that Jake Lang should
despise and dislike Natalie Buchan . . .

A DANGEROUS MAN *by Mary Wibberley*
When Tania met Bryden Kane she realised that he was a
dangerous man to know — certainly she could sense the
danger to her own heart.

APOLLO'S SEED *by Anne Mather*
Martha had been virtually forced to return to Greece and her
husband Dion. But it was clear that his only reason for wanting
her was to get their child back.

A MAN TO WATCH *by Jane Donnelly*
To Harriet, Jotham Gaul was nothing but an irritating boor
who told her she had nothing but her looks — but why should
she care about his opinion?

A CERTAIN SMILE *by Marjorie Lewty*
When Amanda discovered her father, she found herself
whisked into a world of wealth, of tycoons, of sophistication
— and a world that also contained Blair Craddock . . .

STORMY AFFAIR *by Margaret Mayo*
Who did Hamed Ben Slouma think he was, spoiling Amber's
peaceful holiday in Tunisia by whisking her off to his house
and announcing that he was going to marry her?

— all that's pleasurable in Romantic Reading!

Available November 1979

Also available this month
Four Titles in our Mills & Boon
Classics Series

*Specially chosen reissues of the best in
Romantic Fiction*

October's Titles are:

A GIRL ALONE
by Lilian Peake

Sparks had flown between Lorraine Ferrers and Alan Darby from
the moment they met — and it was all Lorraine's fault, for
not trying to conceal her prejudice against him. Then,
unwillingly, she found herself falling in love with him — but
hadn't she left it a little late?

JAKE HOWARD'S WIFE
by Anne Mather

Jake Howard was immensely attractive, immensely rich,
immensely successful. His wife Helen was beautiful, intelligent,
well bred. A perfect couple, in fact, and a perfect marriage,
everyone said. But everyone was wrong . . .

A QUESTION OF MARRIAGE
by Rachel Lindsay

Beth was brokenhearted when Danny Harding let her down,
and vowed that it would be a long time before she fell in love
again. But fall in love again she did — with Danny's cousin
Dean, a very different type of man indeed, and one who
really loved her. Or did he? Surely fate wouldn't be so cruel
as to strike Beth again in the same way?

WHISPERING PALMS
by Rosalind Brett

The discovery of mineral deposits on her African farm came
just at the right time for Lesley, but besides prosperity, it
brought a scheming sister determined to get most of the spoils
herself and to marry the most eligible bachelor in Central
Africa.

Mills & Boon Classics
— all that's great in Romantic Reading!
BUY THEM TODAY

191

192